MEI STRUCTURED MATHEMATICS

THIRD EDITION

Numerical Methods

Richard Lissaman
Elizabeth West

Series Editor: Roger Porkess

HODDER
EDUCATION
AN HACHETTE UK COMPANY

Acknowledgements

We are grateful to the following companies, institutions and individuals who have given permission to reproduce photographs in this book. Every effort has been made to trace and acknowledge ownership of copyright. The publishers will be glad to make suitable arrangements with any copyright holders whom it has not been possible to contact.

OCR, AQA and Edexcel accept no responsibility whatsoever for the accuracy or method of working in the answers given.

Papers used in this book are natural, renewable and recyclable products. They are made from wood grown in sustainable forests. The logging and manufacturing processes conform to the environmental regulations of the country of origin.

Photo (page 1) © Dave Watts/naturepl.com

Orders: please contact Bookpoint Ltd, 130 Milton Park, Abingdon, Oxon OX14 4TD. Telephone: (44) 01235 827720, Fax: (44) 01235 400454. Lines are open from 9 am to 5 pm, Monday to Saturday, with a 24-hour message-answering service. You can also order from our website *www.hoddereducation.co.uk*.

British Library Cataloguing in Publication Data
A catalogue record for this title is available from the The British Library.

ISBN: 978-0-340-81461-1

First Edition published 1993
Second Edition published 2000
Third Edition Published 2004
Impression number   10 9 8 7
Year   2010

Copyright © 2000, 2004, Richard Lissaman and Elizabeth West

Typeset by Pantek Arts Ltd, Maidstone, Kent.
Printed in Malta for Hodder Education, An Hachette UK Company,
338 Euston Road, London NW1 3BH.

S18
67143A

MEI Structured Mathematics

Mathematics is not only a beautiful and exciting subject in its own right but also one that underpins many other branches of learning. It is consequently fundamental to the success of a modern economy.

MEI Structured Mathematics is designed to increase substantially the number of people taking the subject post-GCSE, by making it accessible, interesting and relevant to a wide range of students.

It is a credit accumulation scheme based on 45 hour units which may be taken individually or aggregated to give Advanced Subsidiary (AS) and Advanced GCSE (A Level) qualifications in Mathematics and Further Mathematics. The units may also be used to obtain credit towards other types of qualification.

The course is examined by OCR (previously the Oxford and Cambridge Schools Examination Board) with examinations held in January and June each year.

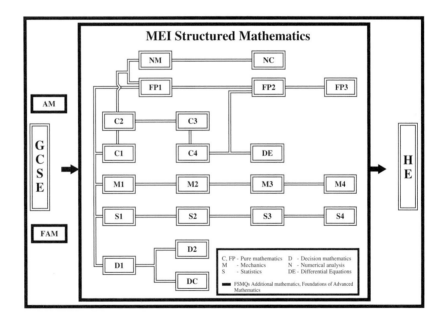

This is one of the series of books written to support the course. Its position within the whole scheme can be seen in the diagram above.

Mathematics in Education and Industry (MEI) is an independent curriculum development body which aims to promote links between education and industry in mathematics MEI produce relevant examination specifications at GCSE, AS and A Level (including Further Mathematics) and for Free Standing Mathematics Qualifications (FSMQs); these are examined by OCR.

In partnership with Hodder Murray, MEI are responsible for three major series of textbooks: Formula One Maths for Key Stage 3, Hodder Mathematics for GCSE and the MEI Structured Mathematics series, including this book, for AS and A Level.

As well as textbooks, MEI take a leading role in the development of on-line resources to support mathematics. The books in this series are complemented by a major MEI website providing full solutions to the exercises, extra questions including on-line multiple choice tests, interactive demonstrations of the mathematics, schemes of work, and much more.

In recent years MEI have worked hard to promote Further Mathematics and, in conjunction with the DfES, they are now establishing the national network of Further Mathematics Centres.

MEI are committed to supporting the professional development of teachers. In addition to a programme of Continual Professional Development, MEI, in partnership with several universities, co-ordinate the Teaching Advanced Mathematics programme, a course designed to give teachers the skills and confidence to teach A Level mathematics successfully.

Much of the work of MEI is supported by the Gatsby Charitable Foundation.

MEI is a registered charity and a charitable company.

MEI's website and email addresses are www.mei.org.uk and office@mei.org.uk.

Introduction

This book has been written to accompany the Numerical Methods module in MEI Structured Mathematics. It replaces two previous editions written by Elizabeth West and is a substantially new book, although some elements of the earlier books have survived. Numerical Methods is now an AS module for Further Mathematics in the MEI specification and this new edition reflects this position. Thus it covers the elementary work in this branch of mathematics and so the book is suitable for use with any introductory course in Numerical Methods.

A graphic calculator or graph-plotting program is an essential aid for this work. All the algorithms studied can be implemented on a spreadsheet and you will learn a lot from setting up a spreadsheet to carry out numerical computation.

In many cases, methods are derived geometrically and a heuristic approach to error analysis is used.

The assessment of the Numerical Methods module includes a piece of coursework. Detailed advice on the requirements is available from the MEI office.

As well as the routine exercises, there are many discussion points to arouse your curiosity. Your ability to analyse and solve problems will improve and hopefully you will find the experience rewarding and satisfying.

I am particularly grateful to Penny Nicholson, Roger Porkess and Neil Sheldon for their guidance and help with reading the text. I would also like to thank all the sixth formers from around Coventry and Warwickshire who pointed out errors in the first draft and OCR for their permission to reproduce a number of past examination questions.

Richard Lissaman

Key to symbols in this book

 This symbol means that you may want to discuss a point with your teacher. If you are working on your own there are answers in the back of the book. It is important, however, that you have a go at answering the questions before looking up the answers if you are to understand the mathematics fully.

 This is a warning sign. It is used where a common mistake, misunderstanding or tricky point is being described.

 This is the ICT icon. It indicates where you should use a graphic calculator or a computer.

 This symbol and a dotted line down the right-hand side of the page indicates material which is beyond the criteria for the unit but which is included for completeness.

☆
☆ Harder questions are indicated with stars. Many of these go beyond the usual examination standard.

Contents

Approximation

Although this may seem a paradox, all exact science is dominated by the idea of approximation.

Bertrand Russell

Approximations

This news story appeared on the BBC's website.

Thousands visit falcon chicks

Thousands of people have been visiting a Devon quarry to view recently-hatched peregrine falcon chicks.

They have become a great attraction, with people visiting in the hope they will see the adult birds feeding their young. The chicks are already growing into adulthood, losing their down which is being replaced with feathers.

The National Trust have set up telescopes and 8000 people have visited to watch the falcons.

As you read this, you realise that the number of people who visited up to the time the article was written was almost certainly not *exactly* 8000.

❷ Why might you suspect that 8000 is probably not the exact value?

Even when you are trying to be precise you often have no option but to give a value only *close to* the exact value. For example, when you measure the width of a room to order a carpet you may only be able to give a value to the nearest centimetre. Such a value is called an *approximation*.

In mathematics you frequently work with models which are simplifications of real-life situations. In mechanics, for example, the effects of air resistance are often ignored. In statistics, you may use a sample from a large quantity of data in order to get an idea of its overall mean. You do this on the understanding that the values you obtain are approximations.

In our number system there are occasions when approximations are a necessity: by Pythogaras's theorem, the diagonal of the unit square has length $\sqrt{2}$.

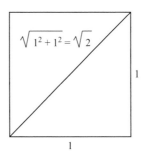

Figure 1.1

You can never input the exact value of $\sqrt{2}$ into a computer because it has an infinitely long decimal expansion. The first 60 decimal places in the decimal expansion of $\sqrt{2}$ are

1.4142135623 7309504880 1688724209 6980785696 7187537694 8073176679

This decimal is *still* only an approximation of $\sqrt{2}$. Most calculators or spreadsheet packages allow only numbers with far fewer decimal places to be input.

Approximations occur for many reasons. Some of these are:

- due to problems with accurate measurement

- as a result of rounding

- due to modelling simplifications

- the necessity of using finite decimals as approximations to certain numbers

- restrictions on the number of decimal places which computing devices will allow

- when getting a more accurate value is not worth the effort.

In this book you will meet various techniques which produce approximations of values. These techniques are called *numerical methods*. The activity below looks at an example of a numerical method.

Here is a way to get an approximation to the square root of a number N.

(i) Begin by choosing a value a_0 close to the square root of N. This is often done by considering which two consecutive square numbers N lies between. For example, if $N = 19$ then because

$$4^2 = 16 \quad \text{and} \quad 5^2 = 25$$

$\sqrt{N}$ must be between 4 and 5. Therefore 4 (or 5) is a reasonable choice for a_0.

(ii) Next calculate the number

$$a_1 = \frac{1}{2}\left(a_0 + \frac{N}{a_0}\right)$$

which is usually a good approximation to $\sqrt{N}$.

Check this by comparing it to the value of $\sqrt{N}$ given by your calculator. For example if $N = 19$ and a_0 is chosen to be 4 then

$$a_1 = \frac{1}{2}\left(4 + \frac{19}{4}\right) = 4.375.$$

The value of $\sqrt{19}$ given by a calculator is 4.358 898 944.

(iii) The approximation a_1 can be used to find an even better value, a_2, where

$$a_2 = \frac{1}{2}\left(a_1 + \frac{N}{a_1}\right).$$

A *sequence* $a_0, a_1, a_2, a_3, \ldots$ of better and better approximations can be produced by doing this over and over again.

Taking the example of $\sqrt{19}$ this gives the following values.

$a_0 = 4$
$a_1 = 4.375$
$a_2 = 4.358\,928\,571$
$a_3 = 4.358\,898\,944$
$a_4 = 4.358\,898\,944$
$a_5 = 4.358\,898\,944$

You can see that after only a few terms the values settle down to the value given by the calculator for $\sqrt{19}$.

Many of the numerical methods you will learn about in this book produce a sequence of numbers which get closer and closer to the value of which you need an approximation. By comparing the terms in the sequence you can sometimes judge how close they are to the value they are heading towards.

Error

In the 2001 Census the population of the UK was recorded as 58 789 194. This is the *exact value* (if you ignore missing or inaccurately completed census forms) giving the size of the population at the time of the census. In many news reports or books of statistics the population of the UK is given as 60 000 000. This is an *approximation* of the exact value. The *error* in this approximation is

60 000 000 – 58 789 194 = 1 210 806.

This is an example of the general situation where the error is defined to be the difference between the approximation and the exact value. Specifically, if the exact value is x and the approximation is X then

error $= X - x$.

So the error is a measure of the distance between the estimate and the exact value and its sign tells you whether the approximation is an underestimate or an overestimate. If X is an overestimate, in other words $X > x$, then the error is positive. If X is an underestimate, i.e. $X < x$, then the error is negative.

Here are some more examples.

Exact value, x	Approximation, X	Error, $X - x$
2.845	2.8	−0.045
5.1245	5.1	−0.0245
9496	9500	4
0.00009	0.0001	0.00001

Absolute error

Often you are only interested in the size of the error and not whether the error is positive or negative. For this reason, the absolute error is defined to be the absolute value of the error. If the exact value is x, and the approximation is X then

$$\text{absolute error} = |\text{error}| = |X - x| = \begin{cases} X - x & \text{if } X \geqslant x \\ x - X & \text{if } x > X \end{cases}.$$

For example, if $x = 5.1245$ and $X = 5.1$ then

$$\begin{aligned} \text{absolute error} &= |X - x| \\ &= |5.1 - 5.1245| \\ &= |-0.0245| \\ &= 0.0245. \end{aligned}$$

Relative error

If the value $X = 0.0001$ is used as an approximation of $x = 0.00009$, the error is 0.00001. This looks very tiny but it is actually nearly 10% of the exact value, x. By contrast, the error when $X = 9500$ is used as an approximation of $x = 9496$ is around only 0.04% of the actual value. (Notice we are even using approximations in this discussion of approximations!)

This is an important consideration when dealing with error. An error of 0.1 metres in the measurement of a window frame could have serious consequences, but an error of 0.1 metres in the measurement of the distance by road from London to Bristol would be trivial. For such reasons you are often more concerned with the *relative error*. This is the ratio of the error to the exact value, defined by

$$\text{relative error} = \frac{X - x}{x} \quad (\text{if } x \neq 0).$$

Absolute relative error

Finally, there is the *absolute relative error* which is the ratio of the size of the error to the magnitude of the exact value, defined by

$$\text{absolute relative error} = \left| \frac{X - x}{x} \right| \quad (\text{if } x \neq 0).$$

This means that (for $x \neq 0$)

$$\text{absolute relative error} = \begin{cases} \dfrac{X - x}{|x|} & \text{if } X > x \\ \dfrac{x - X}{|x|} & \text{if } X < x \end{cases}$$

Sometimes absolute relative error is expressed as a percentage and is called *percentage error*. Some examples are given below.

Exact value	Approximation	Error	Absolute error	Relative error	Absolute relative error	Percentage error
2.845	2.8	−0.045	0.045	−0.015 817	0.015 817	1.5817%
5.1245	5.1	−0.0245	0.0245	−0.004 78	0.004 78	0.478%
9496	9500	4	4	0.000 42	0.000 42	0.042%
0.00011	0.0001	−0.000 01	0.000 01	−0.091	0.091	9.1%

⚠ In this book, all angles are measured in *radians*, unless otherwise stated. You may not have met radians in your pure mathematics course yet.

Radians are used extensively in mathematics because they simplify many calculations. The radian is sometimes referred to as the natural unit of angular measure.

Many calculators have a mode called 'rad'. Set your calculator to this mode when working with trigonometrical functions where angles are given in radians.

If, as in figure 1.2, the arc AB of a circle centre O is drawn so that it is equal in length to the radius of the circle, then the angle AOB is 1 radian, about 57.3°.

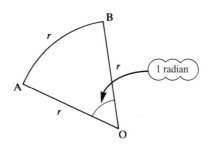

Figure 1.2

Since the circumference of a circle is given by $2\pi r$, it follows that the angle of a complete turn is 2π radians

$$360° = 2\pi \text{ radians.}$$

Consequently

$$180° = \pi \text{ radians}$$

$$90° = \frac{\pi}{2} \text{ radians}$$

$$60° = \frac{\pi}{3} \text{ radians}$$

$$45° = \frac{\pi}{4} \text{ radians}$$

$$30° = \frac{\pi}{6} \text{ radians, etc.}$$

To convert degrees into radians you multiply by $\frac{\pi}{180}$. To convert radians into degrees multipy by $\frac{180}{\pi}$.

Notes

1   If an angle is a simple fraction or multiple of 180° and you wish to give its value in radians, it is usual to leave the answer as a fraction of π.

2   When an angle is given as a multiple of π it is assumed to be in radians.

EXAMPLE 1.1

For small values of x (with x in radians), the following can be used as an approximation of sin x.

$$\sin x \approx x - \frac{x^3}{6}$$

(The symbol in the middle of this expression means 'is approximately the same as'.)

Taking the value that your calculator gives you for sin 0.1 as the exact value, work out the error and relative error when this formula is used to approximate sin 0.1.

SOLUTION

A calculator gives a value of 0.099 833 417 for sin 0.1.

Putting $x = 0.1$ into the formula gives the following approximation to sin 0.1.

$$x - \frac{x^3}{6} = 0.1 - \frac{0.1^3}{6}$$

$$= 0.099 833 333$$

Taking the exact value as the one given by the calculator, the error in this approximation is

$$\text{approximation} - \text{exact value} = 0.099 833 333 - 0.099 833 417$$
$$= -0.000 000 084.$$

The relative error in this approximation is

$$\frac{\text{approximation} - \text{exact value}}{\text{exact value}} = \frac{0.099\,833\,333 - 0.099\,833\,417}{0.099\,833\,417}$$

$$= -0.000\,000\,841.$$

Rounding numbers

Rounding is a way to simplify or shorten a number in a situation where the full level of accuracy is not necessary.

Usually quantities are rounded to a certain number of decimal places or a certain number of significant figures. The rounded figure is then an approximation to the original number and as such it has an error.

The following examples show rounding to a number of decimal places and the error incurred.

EXAMPLE 1.2

(i) Round 48.7564 to 2 decimal places.

(ii) Calculate the error in the rounded figure.

SOLUTION

(i) 48.75⑥4   *Look at the third decimal place. Since it is greater than 5 round up.*

Answer = 48.76

(ii) Error = Approximation − Exact value

$$= 48.76 - 48.7564$$

$$= 0.0036$$

When rounding has taken place it is usual to write the number of decimal places (d.p.) to which the figure has been rounded. Not only does this tell the reader about the accuracy of the approximation, it also emphasises the fact that the number actually *is* an approximation. For the example above you would write 48.76 (to 2 d.p.).

The method of rounding a number to a specified number of significant figures is similar.

EXAMPLE 1.3

(i) Round 690 345 to 4 significant figures.

(ii) Calculate the error in the rounded figure.

SOLUTION

(i) 690 3④5   *Look at the fifth digit. Since it is less than 5 round down.*

Answer = 690 300

(ii) Error = Approximation − Exact value

$$= 690\,300 - 690\,345$$

$$= -45$$

It is usual to write the number of significant figures (s.f.) to which a figure has been rounded after it. In the last example you would write 690 300 (to 4 s.f.). This distinguishes it from the exact value 690 300 and from 690 300 (to 5 s.f.), for example, which would indicate it was an approximation to an exact value x with $69\,295 \leqslant x < 69\,305$.

⚠️ A common mistake is to round via a series of roundings of the last decimal place. Take the number 3.345 67 for example. If you continually round the final decimal place until you have only one decimal place left, you get the following series of values.

$$3.345\,67 \rightarrow 3.3457 \rightarrow 3.346 \rightarrow 3.35 \rightarrow 3.4$$

However, when rounding 3.345 67 to 1 decimal place only the second decimal place should be considered. As this is 4, you should round down to give 3.3 (1 d.p.). This is the correct answer and it is different from the figure obtained by progressive rounding.

❓ (i) When an exact value x is rounded to 1 decimal place to produce an approximation X, what is the maximum absolute error that can be incurred?

(ii) What is the maximum possible absolute error which can be incurred when a number is rounded to 2 decimal places?

(iii) Find a formula, in terms of n, which gives the maximum possible absolute error incurred when a number is rounded to n decimal places?

(iv) Is it possible to find a formula for the maximum possible absolute error incurred when a number is rounded to n significant figures?

EXERCISE 1A   **1** Copy and complete the following table.

Exact value	Approximation	Error	Absolute error	Relative error	Absolute relative error	Percentage error
129.28	130					
32.3	32					
0.0078	0.008					
0.0078	0.01					
2 000 234	2 000 000					

2 Round the following numbers to
   (a) 3 decimal places
   (b) 3 significant figures.

   (i) $\frac{1}{64}$ (ii) $\frac{1}{101}$ (iii) $2\frac{2}{3}$ (iv) $3\frac{4}{7}$

3 Round each of these numbers to the number of significant figures shown
   in brackets.
   (i) 0.012 47 (3)   (ii) 28 421.1 (4)
   (iii) 107.144 (2)   (iv) 91.488   (4)
   (v) 7.429 99 (5)   (vi) 0.001 418 (3)

4 The exact population of Avonford is 26 392.
   Calculate the error in the approximation of this value obtained by rounding
   it to
   (i)   1 significant figure   (ii) 2 significant figures
   (iii) 3 significant figures   (iv) 4 significant figures.

5 Taking the value of $\sqrt{2}$ given by your calculator as the exact value (of course
   this is just an approximation to $\sqrt{2}$ which actually has an infinitely long
   decimal expansion), calculate the relative error in the approximation, to
   $\sqrt{2}$ given by rounding it to
   (i)   1 decimal place   (ii) 2 decimal places
   (iii) 3 decimal places   (iv) 4 decimal places.

6 The following values are all approximations to π.

   $$\sqrt[3]{31}, \frac{22}{7}, 154^{\frac{5}{22}} \text{ and } 43^{\frac{7}{23}}$$

   By calculating the absolute error in each of them (using the value of π given by
   your calculator as the exact value) list them in order from the least accurate to
   the most accurate.

7 For small values of x, with x in radians, the following formula can be used
   as an approximation of $\cos x$.

   $$\cos x \approx 1 - \frac{x^2}{2}$$

   Taking the value that your calculator gives you for $\cos 0.1$ as the exact value,
   work out the error and relative error when this formula is used to approximate
   $\cos 0.1$.

Interval estimates

Think about the following statement.

> The value x, correct to 1 decimal place, is 1.5.

This means that if you were to round x to 1 decimal place the answer would be 1.5. What does this tell you about x?

The numbers that round to 1.5 to 1 decimal place are those between 1.45 and 1.55, including 1.45 but not including 1.55. So x could be any of these numbers. You can write this as follows.

$$1.45 \leqslant x < 1.55.$$

This is an example of an *interval*. This interval is sometimes written as [1.45, 1.55). The square bracket means that 1.45 is included in the interval and the round bracket means that 1.55 is not included in the interval. The number 1.45 is said to be a *lower bound* for x and the number 1.55 is an *upper bound*.

Any statement which says that an exact value x is between two values is called an *interval estimate* for x. So the statement above is an example of an interval estimate.

Historical note

An early example of an interval estimate appears in Archimedes' 'The Measurement of the Circle'. He inscribed a regular 96-sided shape both inside and outside a circle with diameter 1 to approximate the value of π. By calculating the perimeter of each shape he reported that 'The ratio of the circumference of any circle to its diameter is less than $3\frac{1}{7}$ but greater than $3\frac{10}{71}$.'

 To clarify, when a value x is said to be '1.83 correct to 2 decimal places' or '1.83 to 2 decimal places', what is meant is that when x is rounded to 2 decimal places it gives the value 1.83. The statements '$x = 1.83$ (to 2 d.p.)' and '$X = 1.83$ is an approximation to x which is correct to 2 decimal places' also mean the same thing.

Similarly if a value x is said to be '4130 correct to 3 significant figures' or '4130 to 3 significant figures', what is meant is that when x is rounded to 3 significant figures it gives the value 4130. The statements '$x = 4130$ (to 3 s.f.)' and '$X = 4130$ is an approximation to x which is correct to 3 significant figures' also mean the same thing.

EXAMPLE 1.4

An approximate value of the population of a country is given as 32 000 000 and is said to be correct to 2 significant figures.

(i) Give an interval estimate for the exact value of the population.

(ii) What is the maximum possible absolute error in this approximation?

SOLUTION

(i) The approximation $X = 32\,000\,000$ of the exact value of the population, x, is correct to 2 significant figures. This gives the following interval estimate for x.

$$31\,500\,000 \leqslant x < 32\,500\,000$$

(ii) Since x is a whole number this means that

$$31\,500\,000 \leqslant x \leqslant 32\,499\,999.$$

The maximum possible absolute error is 500 000, which would be the case if $x = 31\,500\,000$.

EXAMPLE 1.5

A measuring device is known to give an absolute relative error less than or equal to 0.05 in any measurement it produces.
The device measures a length as 399 cm.
Give an interval estimate for the exact length, x.

SOLUTION

If the approximation $X = 399$ is an overestimate to the exact length, x, with a relative error of 0.05 then

$$\frac{339 - x}{x} = 0.05.$$

Rearranging this gives

$$399 = 1.05x$$

$$x = \frac{399}{1.05} = 380.$$

If the approximation is an underestimate with a relative error of 0.05 then

$$\frac{x - 339}{x} = 0.05.$$

Rearranging this gives

$$399 = 0.95x$$

$$x = \frac{339}{0.95} = 420.$$

So an interval estimate for x is $380 \leqslant x \leqslant 420$.

Approximations from interval estimates

If you have an interval estimate for a value it may be possible to give that value correct to some number of decimal places. The next example illustrates this.

EXAMPLE 1.6

An interval estimate for x is $1.13 < x < 1.141$.
Give x correct to the maximum number of decimal places you can.

SOLUTION

All the numbers between 1.13 and 1.141 round to 1.1 to 1 decimal place.
Therefore x is 1.1 to 1 decimal place.
It is not possible to say what x is to 2 decimal places. It could be either 1.13 or 1.14.

Given only an interval estimate for an exact value, the mid-point of that interval can be no further than half the length of the interval from the exact value. For this reason the mid-point is often taken as an approximation to the exact value. This is shown in the next example.

EXAMPLE 1.7

An interval estimate for x is $7.8 \leqslant x \leqslant 8.0$.
Give an approximation to x which has the smallest possible maximum absolute error.

SOLUTION

Figure 1.3 shows that the mid-point of the interval, 7.9, is no further than 0.1 from the exact value.

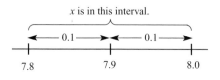

Figure 1.3

In other words, $X = 7.9$ is an approximation to x with a maximum possible absolute error of 0.1.

EXAMPLE 1.8

An interval estimate for x is $1.2 \leqslant x \leqslant 1.6$.
The value $X = 1.4$ is used as an approximation to x.

(i) What is the maximum possible absolute error in the approximation $X = 1.4$?
(ii) What is the maximum possible absolute relative error in the approximation $X = 1.4$?

SOLUTION

(i) The maximum possible absolute error is 0.2, which would be the case if $x = 1.2$ or $x = 1.6$.

(ii) If $x = 1.2$ then the absolute relative error is

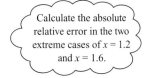

Calculate the absolute relative error in the two extreme cases of $x = 1.2$ and $x = 1.6$.

$$\frac{X - x}{x} = \frac{1.4 - 1.2}{1.2}$$

$$= \frac{0.2}{1.2} = \frac{1}{6}.$$

If $x = 1.6$ then the absolute relative error is

$$\frac{x - X}{x} = \frac{1.6 - 1.4}{1.6}$$

$$= \frac{0.2}{1.6} = \frac{1}{8}.$$

So the maximum possible absolute relative error is $\frac{1}{6}$, which would occur if $x = 1.2$.

EXERCISE 1B

1 In each case below give x to as many decimal places as is possible using the information given.

(i) $1.45 < x < 1.545$

(ii) $3.893 < x \leqslant 3.896$

(iii) $78.900\,01 \leqslant x \leqslant 78.900\,02$

(iv) $56.734 < x \leqslant 56.7345$

2 In each case below give x to as many significant figures as is possible using the information given.

(i) $100 < x < 110$

(ii) $7856 < x \leqslant 7864$

(iii) $5140 \leqslant x \leqslant 5210$

(iv) $58\,000\,780 < x \leqslant 58\,001\,280$

3 The value 3.1 is an approximation of a certain value which is correct to 1 decimal place.

(i) Give an interval estimate for the exact value.

(ii) What is the maximum possible absolute error in this approximation?

4 An approximation to the number of people at a football match is given as 32 300 and it is said to be correct to 3 significant figures.
Give an interval estimate for the exact number of people, x, at the match.

5 It is known that $0.78 < x < 0.788$.
With only this information a student claims that x is 0.78 correct to 2 decimal places.
Can he be sure of this?

6 An interval estimate for x is $23.91 \leqslant x \leqslant 23.99$.
Give an approximation to x which has the smallest possible maximum absolute error.

7 In each case below an approximation, X, is given to an exact value along with the maximum possible absolute error, m, in that approximation.

In each case give an interval estimate for the exact value, x.

(i) $X = 60$, $m = 4$

(ii) $X = 79.8$, $m = 0.05$

(iii) $X = 0.9999$, $m = 0.0001$

8 An interval estimate for x is $8 \leqslant x \leqslant 10$.

The value $X = 9$ is used as an approximation to x.

(i) What is the maximum possible absolute error in the approximation X?

(ii) What is the maximum possible absolute relative error in the approximation X?

9 An interval estimate for x is $0.2 \leqslant x \leqslant 0.24$.

The value $X = 0.22$ is used as an approximation to x.

(i) What is the maximum possible absolute error in the approximation X?

(ii) What is the maximum possible absolute relative error in the approximation X?

10 An approximation to the length of a cross-country course is said to be 5.5 km. The absolute relative error in this approximation is known to be less than or equal to 0.1.

The race organisers require that the cross-country course is at least 5 km in length.

Can they be sure that it satisfies this condition?

11 The height of a cliff can be approximated by dropping a stone over the edge and timing how long it takes to hit the water below.

The height in metres, h, can be calculated using the formula

$$h = \tfrac{1}{2}gt^2 \; \text{\textcircled{$\star$}}$$

where t is the time in seconds and g is a constant.

The exact numerical value of g is 9.8 but it is often rounded to 10 for convenience.

(i) For one calculation, t is measured as 4 and g is rounded to 10. State the relative error in this approximation of g, and show that it is equal to the relative error in the subsequent approximation of h provided the value $t = 4$ is exact.

(ii) For a second calculation, g is taken as 9.8, and the time is measured as 5 seconds, correct to the nearest second.

Find the value of h using these values as given by $\text{\textcircled{$\star$}}$ and find also the range within which the true value of h lies.

(iii) Find for this second calculation, the maximum possible absolute relative error in the value of h given by $\text{\textcircled{$\star$}}$.

[MEI, *part*]

Doing arithmetic with approximations

You should try to be aware of situations in which you are using an approximation and of the consequences of doing so.

Often calculations are done using approximate values. What degree of accuracy is to be expected in the results of such calculations?

For example, if the number x is 0.5 correct to 1 decimal place and y is 0.62 correct to 2 decimal places then how accurate is $0.5 + 0.62 = 1.12$ as an approximation to $x + y$?

The information you have gives the following interval estimates for x and y.

$$0.45 \leqslant x < 0.55 \quad \text{and} \quad 0.615 \leqslant y < 0.625$$

From this you can calculate a lower bound for $x + y$ and an upper bound for $x + y$ and so get an interval estimate for $x + y$.

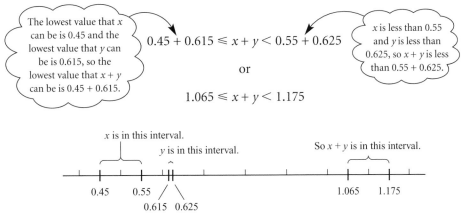

The lowest value that x can be is 0.45 and the lowest value that y can be is 0.615, so the lowest value that $x + y$ can be is $0.45 + 0.615$.

$$0.45 + 0.615 \leqslant x + y < 0.55 + 0.625$$

x is less than 0.55 and y is less than 0.625, so $x + y$ is less than $0.55 + 0.625$.

or

$$1.065 \leqslant x + y < 1.175$$

x is in this interval.
y is in this interval.
So $x + y$ is in this interval.

0.45 0.55 0.615 0.625   1.065 1.175

Figure 1.4

Therefore, with the information that you have, you cannot give an approximation of $x + y$ which is correct even to one decimal place! $x + y$ could round to 1.1 or it could round to 1.2.

The value 1.12 certainly *cannot* be said to be correct to 2 decimal places. This should act as a cautionary example when doing arithmetic with approximations.

In the next example, adding, subtracting and dividing values for which interval estimates are available is considered.

EXAMPLE 1.9

It is known that $3.2 \leqslant x \leqslant 3.3$ and that $11 \leqslant y \leqslant 12.8$.
Find an interval estimate for each of the following.

(i) $x + y$

(ii) $y - x$

(iii) $\dfrac{x}{y}$

SOLUTION

(i) The lowest value that x can be is 3.2 and the lowest value that y can be is 11.
Therefore the lowest value that $x + y$ can be is $3.2 + 11 = 14.2$.
This can be written as follows.

$$x + y \geqslant 3.2 + 11 = 14.2$$

The highest value that x can be is 3.3 and the highest value that y can be is 12.8.
Therefore the highest value that $x + y$ can be is $3.3 + 12.8 = 16.1$.
As an inequality this is,

$$x + y \leqslant 3.3 + 12.8 = 16.1.$$

Therefore an interval estimate of $x + y$ is

$$14.2 \leqslant x + y \leqslant 16.1.$$

(ii) The lowest value of $y - x$ happens when y is the lowest value it can be, 11, and x is the highest value it can be, 3.3. This can be expressed as

$$y - x \geqslant 11 - 3.3 = 7.7.$$

The highest value of $y - x$ happens when y takes its highest possible value, 12.8, and x takes its lowest possible value, 3.2. You can write this as

$$y - x \leqslant 12.8 - 3.2 = 9.6.$$

So an interval estimate of $y - x$ is $7.7 \leqslant y - x \leqslant 9.6$.

(iii) The lowest possible value of $\dfrac{x}{y}$ happens when x takes its lowest possible value and y takes its highest possible value.

This would be $\dfrac{3.2}{12.8} = 0.25$.

The highest value of $\dfrac{x}{y}$ happens when x takes its highest possible value and y takes its lowest possible value.

This would be $\dfrac{3.3}{11} = 0.3$.

Therefore an interval estimate of $\dfrac{x}{y}$ is $0.25 \leqslant \dfrac{x}{y} \leqslant 0.3$.

Subtraction of nearly equal quantities

One particular situation in which there may be a loss of *many* significant figures in accuracy is when nearly equal quantities are subtracted. This is illustrated in the following example.

EXAMPLE 1.10

The values $X = 123.453$ and $Y = 120.351$ are approximations to values x and y which are both correct to 6 significant figures.
Give $x - y$ correct to as many significant figures as is possible with this information.

SOLUTION

Since $X = 123.453$ is correct to 6 significant figures

$$123.4525 \leqslant x < 123.4535.$$

Similarly, since $Y = 120.351$ is correct to 6 significant figures

$$120.3505 \leqslant y < 120.3515.$$

Therefore

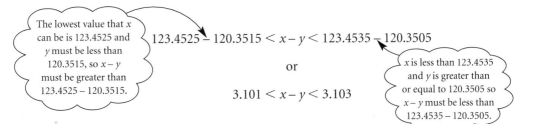

The lowest value that x can be is 123.4525 and y must be less than 120.3515, so $x - y$ must be greater than $123.4525 - 120.3515$.

$$123.4525 - 120.3515 < x - y < 123.4535 - 120.3505$$

or

$$3.101 < x - y < 3.103$$

x is less than 123.4535 and y is greater than or equal to 120.3505 so $x - y$ must be less than $123.4535 - 120.3505$.

So $x - y$ must be 3.10 to 3 significant figures, but it cannot be given to 4 significant figures from the information available.

EXERCISE 1C

1 It is known that $4.0 \leqslant x \leqslant 4.5$ and that $10.31 \leqslant y \leqslant 10.45$.
Find an interval estimate of each of the following.
(i) $x + y$ (ii) $y - x$
(iii) xy (iv) $\dfrac{x}{y}$

2 The value $X = 340$ is an approximation of an integer x which is correct to 2 significant figures and $Y = 72\,100$ is an approximation of an integer y which is correct to 3 significant figures.
Find an interval estimate of each of the following and hence give each value correct to the maximum number of significant figures possible.
(i) $x + y$ (ii) $y - x$
(iii) xy (iv) $\dfrac{x}{y}$

3 The value $X = 0.312$ is an approximation of x which is correct to 3 decimal places and $Y = 0.21$ is an approximation of y which is correct to 2 decimal places. Give an interval estimate of each of the following and hence give each to the maximum number of decimal places possible.

(i) x (ii) y

(iii) $x + y$ (iv) $x - y$

(v) $x + 2y$ (vi) $\dfrac{x}{y}$

(vii) $x^2 y$

4 The exact value of a is 1.234 54 and the exact value of b is 1.234 55. These values are rounded to 4 decimal places and the subsequent approximations are used to approximate $b - a$.
Calculate the percentage error in this approximation.

5 A student finds estimates to the roots α, β of the quadratic equation $ax^2 + bx + c = 0$ using the following algorithm.

> **Step 1**   Calculate $d = \sqrt{b^2 - 4ac}$ correct to 4 significant figures.
>
> **Step 2**   Calculate $\alpha = \dfrac{-b - d}{2a}$.
>
> **Step 3**   Calculate $\beta = -\left(\dfrac{b}{a} + \alpha\right)$.

In a particular case, $a = 1$, $b = -50$, $c = 1$.

(i)   Obtain the values d, α and β as found by the student.
Solve the equation correct to 6 decimal places using the usual formula for the roots of a quadratic and use the values you get to determine the relative errors in the values of α and β found by the student.

A second student uses this algorithm.

> **Step 1**   Calculate $d = \sqrt{b^2 - 4ac}$ correct to 4 significant figures.
>
> **Step 2**   Calculate $\beta = \dfrac{-b + d}{2a}$.
>
> **Step 3**   Calculate $\alpha = \dfrac{c}{a\beta}$.

(ii) Obtain the values α and β as found by the second student.

(iii) Identify and explain two features of the second student's algorithm which make it better than the first.

[**MEI**, *part*]

6 The refractive index, r, of a medium is determined by measuring two angles, a and β, and using the formula

$$r = \frac{\sin a}{\sin \beta}.$$

(i) Find the calculated value of r if $a = 37°$ and $\beta = 31°$.

Calculate the interval within which the true value of r lies if the values of a and β are to the nearest degree.

Hence

(a) determine the maximum possible magnitude of the relative error in the calculated value of r

(b) state the number of significant figures to which the value of r can be given with certainty.

(ii) Suppose now that $a = 37°$ and $\beta = 31°$, each measured correct to the nearest $0.5°$.

Determine the number of significant figures to which r can now be given with certainty.

(iii) Determine the accuracy to which it would be necessary to measure a and β (still taken to be $37°$ and $31°$) in order for r to be known correct to 3 significant figures.

[MEI]

Propagation of relative error when multiplying or dividing approximations

In general if X is an approximation of the exact value x and Y is an approximation of y then it seems sensible to ask what happens if XY is used as an approximation of xy and $\frac{X}{Y}$ is used as an approximation of $\frac{x}{y}$.

EXAMPLE 1.11   Suppose that $X = 1.3$ is used as an approximation to $x = 1.3478$ and $Y = 0.03$ is used an approximation to $y = 0.0297$.

(i) What is the relative error in each of these approximations?

(ii) What is the relative error when XY is used an approximation of xy?

(iii) What is the relative error when $\frac{X}{Y}$ is used as an approximation of $\frac{x}{y}$?

Find any relationships between the values you have calculated.

SOLUTION

(i) The relative error when X is used to approximate x is

$$r_1 = \frac{X - x}{x}$$

$$= \frac{1.3 - 1.3478}{1.3478} = -0.035\,47 \text{ (to 5 d.p.).}$$

The relative error when Y is used to approximate y is

$$r_2 = \frac{Y - y}{y}$$

$$= \frac{0.03 - 0.0297}{0.0297}$$

$$= 0.010\,10 \text{ (to 5 d.p.).}$$

(ii) The relative error when XY is used to approximate xy is

$$r_3 = \frac{XY - xy}{xy}$$

$$= \frac{(1.3 \times 0.03) - (1.3478 \times 0.0297)}{1.3478 \times 0.0297}$$

$$= \frac{0.039 - 0.400\,296\,6}{0.400\,296\,6} = -0.025\,72 \text{ (to 5 d.p.).}$$

A possible relationship is that $r_1 + r_2 = -0.0237$ is approximately equal to this value.

(iii) The relative error when $\dfrac{X}{Y}$ is used to approximate $\dfrac{x}{y}$ is

$$r_4 = \frac{\dfrac{X}{Y} - \dfrac{x}{y}}{\dfrac{x}{y}}$$

$$= \frac{\dfrac{1.3}{0.03} - \dfrac{1.3478}{0.0297}}{\dfrac{1.3478}{0.0297}}$$

$$= \frac{43.333\,33 - 45.380\,471\,38}{45.380\,471\,38} = -0.045\,11 \text{ (to 5 d.p.).}$$

A possible relationship is that $r_1 - r_2 = -0.035\,47 - 0.010\,10 = -0.045\,57$ (to 5 d.p.) is approximately equal to this value.

In fact the observations made in the example above hold in general.

If X is an approximation of x with relative error r_1 and Y is an approximation of y with relative error r_2 then

- the relative error in XY as an approximation of xy is approximately $r_1 + r_2$
- the relative error in $\dfrac{X}{Y}$ as an approximation of $\dfrac{x}{y}$ is approximately $r_1 - r_2$.

❓ The relative error in $\dfrac{X}{Y}$ as an approximation to $\dfrac{x}{y}$ is approximately $r_1 - r_2$. Does this mean that this approximation is 'better' than both of the approximations of x and y?

Think about the following cases, taking X, x, Y and y all to be positive for simplicity.

In each case, consider the value $\dfrac{X}{Y}$ and then consider the sign of r_1 and r_2 and what this means for $r_1 - r_2$.

(i) X is an overestimate and Y is an underestimate.

(ii) X is an underestimate and Y is an overestimate.

(iii) X and Y are both overestimates.

(iv) X and Y are both underestimates.

Recall that the absolute relative error in an approximation is the modulus of the relative error.

- Therefore, $|r_1|$ is the absolute relative error in X and $|r_2|$ is the absolute relative error in Y.

- The values $|r_1 + r_2|$ and $|r_1 - r_2|$ are approximately equal to the absolute relative error in XY and $\dfrac{X}{Y}$ respectively.

- The two values $|r_1 - r_2|$ and $|r_1 + r_2|$ are *always* less than or equal to $|r_1| + |r_2|$, regardless of whether r_1 and r_2 are positive or negative. (You may wish to experiment with values of r_1 and r_2 to convince yourself that this is true.)

This leads to this important result.

> The absolute relative error in XY as an approximation of xy and in $\dfrac{X}{Y}$ as an approximation of $\dfrac{x}{y}$ is less than or equal to approximately $|r_1| + |r_2|$ where $|r_1|$ is the absolute relative error in X and $|r_2|$ is the absolute relative error in Y.

Ill-conditioned problems

In some problems a small change in the value input can cause a large change in the output as illustrated in figure 1.5. Such problems are said to be *ill-conditioned*.

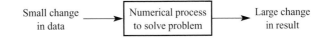

Figure 1.5

Examples of such problems are

(i) $x^2 - 2x + 0.9 = 0$ which has two solutions
but $x^2 - 2x + 1.01 = 0$ has no solution.

(ii) $\left.\begin{array}{l} x - y = 1 \\ 0.9999x - y = 0 \end{array}\right\}$ has solution $x = 10\,000$
                                        $y = 9999$

but $\left.\begin{array}{l} x - y = 1 \\ x - 0.9999y = 0 \end{array}\right\}$ has solution $x = -9999$
                                        $y = -10\,000.$

Since the coefficients in these equations could be data values or could have been obtained from a previous computation and so be subject to errors, the problem of obtaining reliable solutions to the equations is difficult to solve.

Looking at the two examples, in the first, if $f(x) = x^2 - 2x + 0.9$, you see from the graph of the function f in figure 1.6 that f has a turning point very close to the x axis.

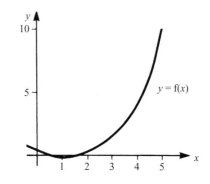

Figure 1.6

It follows that a small change in one of the coefficients could move the turning point above the x axis. Similarly, looking at the equations in **(ii)**, the first can be written as $y = x - 1$ and the second as $y = 0.9999x$; they are represented geometrically by the pair of almost parallel lines, as shown in figure 1.7.

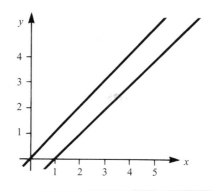

Figure 1.7

A small change in the gradient of one line will make a significant change in the point of intersection. Indeed, they may no longer intersect.

There is no simple rule for handling ill-conditioned problems except the obvious one that in all work associated with the problem, extra figures should be carried to minimise the effects of the rounding error.

EXAMPLE 1.12

Examine the value of $f(x) = \dfrac{1}{1 - x^2}$ for values of x near to 1.

SOLUTION

The values are listed in the following table.

x	$f(x)$	Change in x	Change in f(x)
0.9	5.263 16		
		0.09	44.9881
0.99	50.2513		
		0.009	449.999
0.999	500.250		
		0.0009	4500
0.9999	5000.25		

Thus, a change of 0.0009 in the x value, from $x = 0.999$ to $x = 0.9999$ gives a change of 4500 in the calculated value of $f(x)$, displaying serious ill-conditioning.

In this case, the subtraction of nearly equal numbers is responsible for the ill-conditioned nature of the problem.

❓ Construct similar tables showing the values of $f(x) = \dfrac{1}{1 - x^2}$ for

(i) $x = 1.1, 1.01, 1.001$ and 1.0001 **(ii)** $x = 6.1, 6.01, 6.001$ and 6.0001.

Is ill-conditioning displayed in either of these cases?

Figure 1.8 shows the graph of $f(x) = \dfrac{1}{1 - x^2}$.

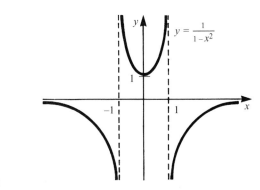

Figure 1.8

❓ How does this graph indicate ill-conditioning near $x = -1$ and $x = 1$?

EXERCISE 1D

1 The value $X = 10.3$ is used as an approximation of $x = 10.278\,78$ and $Y = 5.06$ is used as an approximation $y = 5.0619$.

Calculate the relative errors in each of the following approximations and comment upon any relationships between your answers to parts **(iii)** to **(x)** and your answers to parts **(i)** and **(ii)**.

(i) X as an approximation of x

(ii) Y as an approximation of y

(iii) XY as an approximation of xy

(iv) $\dfrac{X}{Y}$ as an approximation of $\dfrac{x}{y}$

(v) X^2 as an approximation of x^2

(vi) Y^3 as an approximation of y^3

(vii) $3X$ as an approximation of $3x$

(viii) $\dfrac{1}{Y}$ as an approximation of $\dfrac{1}{y}$

(ix) $\dfrac{X^5}{Y^7}$ as an approximation of $\dfrac{x^5}{y^7}$

(x) $\dfrac{2X^2}{3Y}$ as an approximation of $\dfrac{2x^2}{3y}$

2 The number $t = 3.45$ is approximated by $T = 3.5$.

Write down the relative error in T. Calculate the error and relative errors in T^2 and $\sqrt{T}$ as approximations to t^2 and $\sqrt{t}$.

[**MEI**, *part*]

3 For small values of x (with x in radians), the following formula can be used as an approximation of $\tan x$.

$$\tan x \approx x + \frac{x^3}{3}$$

(i)   A student used this formula to approximate $\tan 0.1$.
Taking the value that your calculator gives you for $\tan 0.1$ as the exact value, work out the absolute error in his approximation.

(ii)   A second student calculates approximations to $\sin 0.1$ and $\cos 0.1$ using the formulae

$$\sin x \approx x - \frac{x^3}{6} \quad \text{and} \quad \cos x \approx 1 - \frac{x^2}{2}.$$

She then uses the fact that $\tan 0.1 = \dfrac{\sin 0.1}{\cos 0.1}$ to produce an approximation to $\tan 0.1$.

Compare the absolute error in this student's approximation to that in the first student's.

(iii)   For the second student, what is the relationship between the relative errors in her approximations to $\sin 0.1$, $\cos 0.1$ and $\tan 0.1$?

4 In certain computer applications, a rough approximation is required of $\sqrt{x}$ where $0.25 \leqslant x \leqslant 1$. A formula sometimes used is

$$\sqrt{x} \approx \frac{2}{3}x + 0.36. \;\circledast$$

(i) Find the two values of x for which there is zero error in this approximation.
[Hint: Form a quadratic equation in t, where $t = \sqrt{x}$.]

(ii) Find the absolute and relative errors when the approximation is used for $x = 0.25$ and $x = 0.64$.

If s is the approximation to $\sqrt{x}$ given by $\circledast$, then an improved approximation is given by

$$\frac{s^2 + x}{2s}.$$

(iii) Find the relative error in the improved approximation when $x = 0.25$.

(iv) Suppose that s overestimates $\sqrt{x}$ with a relative error of 0.01.
Write down an equation for s in terms of $\sqrt{x}$.
Hence show that $\dfrac{s^2 + x}{2s}$ is very nearly $1.00005\sqrt{x}$.
State the relative error in the improved approximation.

[MEI]

5 The numbers P_n and Q_n are defined as follows.

$$P_n = (3 + 2\sqrt{2})^n, \qquad Q_n = \sqrt{2}(3 + 2\sqrt{2})^n, \qquad n = 1, 2, 3, \dots$$

(i) Use your calculator to show that P_3 and Q_3 can both be closely approximated by integers.
Find the relative errors in these approximations, and hence show that $\frac{140}{99}$ is a good approximation of $\sqrt{2}$.
Find the relative error in this approximation.
State and explain a relationship between the three relative errors you have found.

(ii) Find similarly another fraction with integers in the numerator and denominator, that is a better approximation of $\sqrt{2}$.

(iii) You are now given that the numbers

$$(3 + 2\sqrt{2})^n + (3 - 2\sqrt{2})^n \quad \text{and} \quad \sqrt{2}(3 + 2\sqrt{2})^n - \sqrt{2}(3 - 2\sqrt{2})^n$$

are exactly equal to integers for $n = 1, 2, 3, \dots$.
By considering the magnitude of $(3 - 2\sqrt{2})^n$ for $n = 1, 2, 3, \dots$, show that P_n and Q_n will be close to integers for all $n > 1$.

[MEI]

1 Whenever an approximation, X, is given to an exact value, x, the error is defined to be

$$\text{error} = X - x$$

and the absolute error is defined to be

$$\text{absolute error} = |\text{error}| = |X - x|.$$

So absolute error $= X - x$ if $X \geqslant x$ and absolute error $= x - X$ if $x > X$.

2 The relative error is sometimes a more useful measure of error. This is defined to be

$$\text{relative error} = \frac{X - x}{x} \quad (\text{if } x \neq 0)$$

and the absolute relative error is defined to be

$$\text{absolute relative error} = \left| \frac{X - x}{x} \right| \quad (\text{if } x \neq 0).$$

3 An interval estimate of an exact value x, is given by a pair of values, a and b, for which either $a < x < b$, $a < x \leqslant b$, $a \leqslant x < b$ or $a \leqslant x \leqslant b$. The number a is said to be a lower bound for x and the number b an upper bound for x.

4 When rounding a number x, to a specified number of decimal places or significant figures, the number with that number of decimal places or significant figures which is closest to x is chosen. In cases when there are two such numbers, round up.

5 When an approximation is said to be correct to a number of decimal places you can give an interval estimate of the exact value. For example, if $X = 3.25$ is an estimate to an exact value x which is correct to 2 decimal places, then x must satisfy $3.245 \leqslant x < 3.255$.

6 When an approximation is said to be correct to a number of significant figures you can give an interval estimate of the exact value. For example, if $X = 14\,300$ is said to be correct to 3 significant figures, the exact value x must satisfy $14\,250 \leqslant x < 14\,350$.

7 If X is an approximation of x with relative error r_1 and Y is an approximation of y with relative error r_2 then XY is an approximation of xy with a relative error of approximately $r_1 + r_2$.

Also $\dfrac{X}{Y}$ is an approximation of $\dfrac{x}{y}$ with a relative error of approximately $r_1 - r_2$.

8 The absolute relative error in XY as an approximation to xy and in $\frac{X}{Y}$ as an approximation of $\frac{x}{y}$ is less than or equal to $|r_1| + |r_2|$ where $|r_1|$ is the absolute relative error in X and $|r_2|$ is the absolute relative error in Y.

9 If the solution to a problem is particularly sensitive to small changes in the data used, the problem is said to be ill-conditioned.

2 The solution of equations

Someone told me that each equation I included in the book would halve the sales.

Stephen Hawking

Usually, the solution of a mathematical problem requires the root of an equation. Some equations, such as $3x + 7 = 34$, $x^2 + 3x + 2 = 0$ and $\sin(3x - 2) = 1$, can be solved using standard methods you may have already studied. However, in many everyday problems the equations turn out to be more complicated.

Think about the problem of calibrating a dipstick to measure the volume of oil in a cylindrical tank which rests on its side (see figure 2.1). The tank has a hole at the top to allow a dipstick to be inserted. Given that the tank is 3 m long and 2 m in diameter, where should the marks be placed on the dipstick to indicate 1, 2, 3, 4, ... m^3 in the tank?

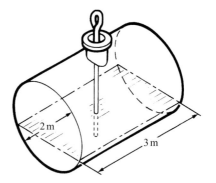

Figure 2.1

As a first step, the volume of the tank can be calculated to be

$$\text{area of cross-section} \times \text{length} = \pi \times 1^2 \times 3 = 3\pi \approx 9.42\,\text{m}^3 \text{ (to 2 d.p.)}$$

The problem is to determine the depth of oil which corresponds to the volumes 1, 2, 3, 4, ... 9 m^3 in the tank.

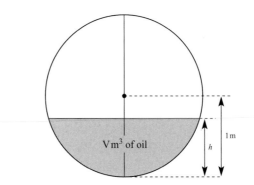

$V\,\text{m}^3$ of oil

h

1 m

Figure 2.2

Using trigonometry it can be shown that the value of h on the dipstick which corresponds to a volume $V\,\text{m}^3$ in the tank (see figure 2.2) is a root of the equation

$$\cos\left((1-h)\sqrt{2h-h^2}+\frac{V}{3}\right)=1-h.$$

This is not a simple equation and it must be solved nine times, with $V = 1, 2, 3, ..., 9$, to determine the position of each mark on the dipstick. For example, to determine the height, h, of the mark for $5\,\text{m}^3$ the equation below must be solved.

$$\cos\left((1-h)\sqrt{2h-h^2}+\frac{5}{3}\right)=1-h.$$

In this chapter you will learn a variety of methods for producing approximations of the roots of such equations. (The dipstick problem appears in Exercise 2B in this chapter.)

Roots of equations and graphs

The roots of an equation are the values of x for which the equation is true. The roots of the equation $x^3 + 4 = 4x^2 + x$ are $x = -1$, $x = 1$ and $x = 4$.

 You can check this very easily. How?

Figure 2.3 shows the graphs of $y = x^3 + 4$ and $y = 4x^2 + x$. Notice that the roots of the equation are the x co-ordinates of the three points, labelled A, B and C, where the graphs intersect.

 Why is this so?

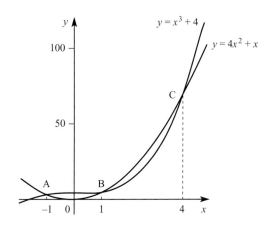

Figure 2.3

The equation

$$x^3 + 4 = 4x^2 + x$$

can be rearranged to give

$$x^3 - 4x^2 - x + 4 = 0.$$

In figure 2.4, the graph of $y = x^3 - 4x^2 - x + 4$ has been added to the diagram. The x co-ordinates of the points where this graph cuts the x axis give the roots of $x^3 - 4x^2 - x + 4 = 0$. Therefore, these values are also the roots of $x^3 + 4 = 4x^2 + x$, as can be seen clearly in figure 2.4.

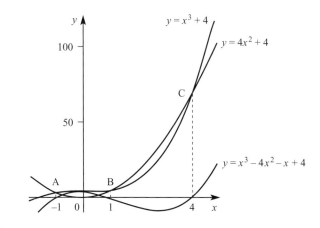

Figure 2.4

 Why does the graph of $y = x^3 - 4x^2 - x + 4$ cross the x axis at the three roots of $x^3 + 4 = 4x^2 + x$?

Finding roots of an equation by looking for sign changes

The solution of the equation

$$x^3 = 10 - 3x$$

is the same as that of $x^3 + 3x - 10 = 0$.

Figure 2.5 shows a graph of the curve $y = f(x)$ where $f(x) = x^3 + 3x - 10$.

It looks as if there is a root, α, of $x^3 + 3x - 10 = 0$ at around $x = 1.7$.

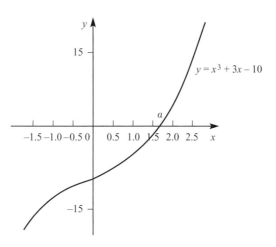

Figure 2.5

To be certain that a is 1.7 correct to 1 decimal place you must make sure that a is greater than or equal to 1.65 and less than 1.75, because all such numbers round to 1.7 to 1 decimal place. This can be written as an interval estimate.

$$1.65 \leqslant a < 1.75$$

You can check whether this is true by looking for a sign change between the values of the function f at the two ends of the interval.

With $f(x) = x^3 + 3x - 10$,

> This is negative, so the graph is below the x axis when $x = 1.65$.

$$f(1.65) = 1.65^3 + (3 \times 1.65) - 10 = -0.557 \dots$$

and

> This is positive, so the graph is above the x axis when $x = 1.75$.

$$f(1.75) = 1.75^3 + (3 \times 1.75) - 10 = +0.609 \dots$$

So a, the point where the graph crosses the x axis, is between $x = 1.65$ and $x = 1.75$. It follows, therefore, that to 1 decimal place, a is 1.7.

? You have two numbers, a and b, with $a < b$ and a function f. If $f(a)$ has the opposite sign to $f(b)$ why would you expect the equation $f(x) = 0$ to have a root between a and b?

This uses a property of a function called *continuity*. A continuous function cannot jump from one value to another without taking all the values in between. In particular, it cannot go from being negative to being positive, or from being positive to being negative, without being zero somewhere in between.

To find the solution of the equation $x^3 = 10 - 3x$ above the equation was rearranged so that it had a zero on one side. That made it possible to locate its root by looking for a change of sign. This is an important technique.

As you will see later, there are lots of methods for finding approximations of roots of equations, some of which call for the equation to be rearranged to a particular form.

EXAMPLE 2.1

Show that 2.60 is an approximation of a root of the equation $x^3 + 2x^2 = 10x + 5$ correct to 2 decimal places.

SOLUTION

The equation $x^3 + 2x^2 = 10x + 5$ can be

rearranged to give $x^3 + 2x^2 - 10x - 5 = 0$.

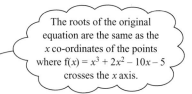

The roots of the original equation are the same as the x co-ordinates of the points where $f(x) = x^3 + 2x^2 - 10x - 5$ crosses the x axis.

A graph of $f(x) = x^3 + 2x^2 - 10x - 5$, showing the root of $f(x) = 0$ at around 2.60 is shown in figure 2.6.

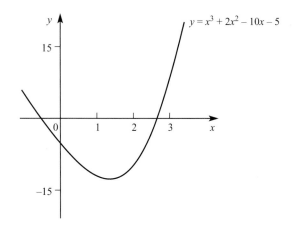

Figure 2.6

If 2.60 is correct to 2 decimal places then the exact value, a, of the root must satisfy

$$2.595 \leqslant a < 2.605.$$

$f(2.595) = -0.007\ldots$

$f(2.605) = +0.200\ldots$

So the graph of the function does cross the x axis somewhere between $x = 2.595$ and $x = 2.605$.

Therefore, the root is between these two values and so will round to 2.60 to 2 decimal places.

EXERCISE 2A

1 Verify that $x = 0.35$ is an approximation of a root of $x^3 - 3x + 1 = 0$ correct to 2 decimal places.

2 Verify that $x = -0.4$ is an approximation of a root of $x^3 + x^2 + 5x + 2 = 0$ correct to 1 decimal place.

3 Verify that $x = 0.62$ is an approximation of a root of $x^3 + 2 = x^2 + 3x$ correct to 2 decimal places.

4 Show, by using a sign-change argument, that 1.4 is an approximation of the positive root of $x^2 - 2 = 0$ with an absolute error of less than 0.05.

5 Verify that $x = 6.7$ radians is an approximation of a root of $\cos x = 2\sin x$ with an absolute error less than 0.05.

6 A root of an equation is known to be between 0.71 and 0.72. With this information only, give an approximation to the root which is correct to as many decimal places as possible and state how many decimal places this is.

7 Write down a function $f(x)$ for which $f(1) > 0$ and $f(4) > 0$, yet the equation ☆ $f(x) = 0$ has a root between $x = 1$ and $x = 4$.
☆ For your function, how many roots does the equation $f(x) = 0$ have between
☆ $x = 1$ and $x = 4$?

The method of bisection

You can rearrange the equation

$$x^4 = 2 - 2x$$

into a form which has a zero on the right-hand side as follows.

$$x^4 + 2x - 2 = 0$$

> As you saw earlier, the solution of this equation is the solution of the original equation and vice versa.

Figure 2.7 shows the graph of the function $f(x) = x^4 + 2x - 2$.

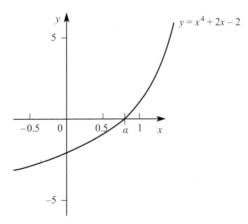

Figure 2.7

The root of an equation can be approximated using a technique called the *method of bisection*. Figure 2.7 shows the root, labelled a, of the function $f(x) = x^4 + 2x - 2$.

The first step when using the method of bisection is to find an interval estimate for the root. This means that you must find two numbers, one that is less than the root and one that is greater than the root.

You can see from figure 2.7 that a is between $x = 0.5$ and $x = 1$, so these are appropriate choices in this case. This is confirmed by finding the value of the function in these cases.

$$f(0.5) = 0.5^4 + 2 \times 0.5 - 2 = -0.9375$$

$$f(1) = 1^4 + 2 \times 1 - 2 = 1$$

So $0.5 < a < 1$ is an interval estimate for a. The values 0.5 and 1.0 are said to *straddle* the root. Remember that 0.5 is said to be a lower bound for x and 1 is said to be an upper bound for x.

To improve this interval estimate try evaluating the function at the value in the middle of these two values, 0.75.

The function is negative here, $f(0.75) = -0.183\ 593\ 75$. Figure 2.8 shows how this helps to locate the root more closely.

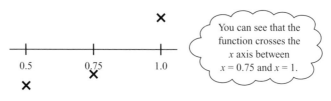

Figure 2.8

So $0.75 < a < 1.0$ is an improved interval estimate for a.

By repeating this process you can continue to improve the interval estimates for a, halving the length of the interval each time. Since $f(0.875)$ is positive, the root a lies between 0.75 and 0.875. The new interval estimate is now $0.75 < a < 0.875$.

The idea is shown the series of diagrams in figure 2.9.

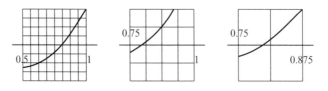

Figure 2.9

You can set out what you have done and continue it further in a table as shown on the next page.

	Step number	Left end of interval		Right end of interval		Mid-point of interval	

All the values between 0.75 and 0.8125 round to 0.8 to 1 decimal place, so a is 0.8 to 1 decimal place.

r	a_r	Sign of $f(a_r)$	b_r	Sign of $f(b_r)$	$c_r = (a_r + b_r) \div 2$	Sign of $f(c_r)$
1	0.500 000	−ve	1.000 000	+ve	0.750 000	−ve
2	0.750 000	−ve	1.000 0 00	+ve	0.875 000	+ve
3	0.750 000	−ve	0.875 000	+ve	0.812 500	+ve
4	0.750 000	−ve	0.81 2 500	+ve	0.781 250	−ve
5	0.781 250	−ve	0.812 500	+ve	0.796 875	−ve
6	0.796 875	−ve	0.812 500	+ve	0.804 688	+ve
7	0.796 875	−ve	0.804 688	+ve	0.800 781	+ve
8	0.796 875	−ve	0.800 781	+ve	0.798 828	+ve

All the values between 0.796 875 and 0.804 688 round to 0.80 to 2 decimal place, so a is 0.80 to 2 decimal places.

As shown above, this information can be used to give an approximation of a to a number of decimal places.

EXAMPLE 2.2

Show that the equation $x^3 + 3x - 5 = 0$ has a root, a, between 1 and 2.
Starting with these two points straddling a, apply the method of bisection three times and give an approximation to a with the smallest maximum absolute error that you can with the information you find.

SOLUTION

Let $f(x) = x^3 + 3x - 5$.

Since $f(1) = -1$ and $f(2) = 9$, there must be a root of $f(x) = 0$ between 1 and 2.

The table shows three applications of the method of bisection beginning with $a_1 = 1$, $b_1 = 2$.

r	a_r	Sign of $f(a_r)$	b_r	Sign of $f(b_r)$	$c_r = (a_r + b_r) \div 2$	Sign of $f(c_r)$
1	1	−ve	2	+ve	1.5	+ve
2	1	−ve	1.5	+ve	1.25	+ve
3	1	−ve	1.25	+ve	1.125	−ve

At this point you see that the root lies between 1.125 and 1.25. The function is negative when $x = 1.125$ and positive when $x = 1.25$.

The mid-point of these two values is 1.1875. Using this as an approximation of the root gives the smallest possible maximum absolute error. Figure 2.10 shows this idea.

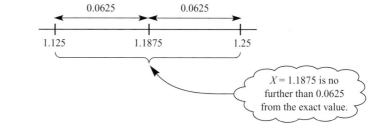

Figure 2.10

Investigate the number of steps of the bisection method required to find an approximation of a root to a given level of accuracy as follows.

1 Show that the equation $x^2 - \sin x - 1 = 0$, where x is in radians, has a root in the interval $[1, 2]$.

2 In the table, $a_1 = 1$ and $b_1 = 2$; these are the left and right values in the first interval estimate.

At each stage, calculate $\varepsilon_r = c_r - a_r$ which is the maximum possible absolute error in the approximation given by the interval mid-point at the rth step. Carry out four steps of the method of bisection and complete the table.

r	a_r	$f(a_r)$	b_r	$f(b_r)$	c_r	$f(c_r)$	ε_r
1	1	−0.8415	2	2.0907	1.5	0.2525	0.5
2							
3							
4							

3 Examine the values in the last column of the table.
What do you notice about these values? Write down the maximum possible error after

(i) 5 steps

(ii) 10 steps

(iii) p steps.

4 How many steps must be carried out so that the maximum possible absolute error is reduced to less than 0.000 001?

EXERCISE 2B

1 Show graphically that the equation $x^3 - x - 1$ has exactly one root in the interval $[1, 2]$.
Use the bisection method to obtain an approximation of this root which is correct to 1 decimal place.

2 Show graphically that the equation $x^5 + 3x^3 - 1 = 0$ has only one root.
Use the bisection method to find an approximation of this root with an error of less than 0.05.

3 Show that the equation $x = \tan x$ has a solution which lies in the interval $[4, 4.5]$. Use the method of bisection to find an approximation of this solution which is correct to 1 decimal place.
Remember the angle is measured in radians.

4 Both of the equations
(i) $x^3 + 0.5x^2 - 0.5x - 1.5 = 0$
(ii) $1.5x\cos x - \sin x = 0$
have a root near to $x = 1$.

Use the method of bisection to find an approximation of each of these roots which is correct to 1 decimal place.

5 Use the method of bisection to find an approximation of the root of the equation $x^4 = 3x - 1$ between 1 and 2 which is correct to 1 decimal place.

6 The equation

$$\cos\left((1 - h) \sqrt{2h - h^2} + \tfrac{1}{3}\right) = 1 - h$$

has a root in the interval $[0.32, 0.33]$.
Use the method of bisection to find an approximation of this solution which is correct to 3 decimal places.
(This is the dipstick problem with $V = 1$ described at the start of this chapter. The angle is measured in radians.)

7 (i) Show that the equation

$$\frac{x(x^{10} - 1)}{x - 1} = 14$$

has a root in the interval $(1.01, 1.09)$.

(ii) Use the bisection method to find an interval (a, b) that contains the root and for which $b - a = 0.01$.

Give the best possible estimate of the root at this stage and state the maximum possible absolute error in that estimate.

[MEI, *part*]

8 (i) **(a)** Show carefully that the equation

$$x^3 + x - 1 = 0$$

has only one real root, and that this root lies between 0 and 1.

(b) Carry out three steps of the bisection method to obtain an estimate of the root.
State the maximum possible error in this estimate.
Determine how many further steps of the bisection method would be needed to reduce the maximum possible error to less than 0.005.

(ii) **(a)** The number A is an approximation to the number a.
It is known that A is correct to 2 decimal places.
State the maximum possible error in A.

(b) The number B is an approximation to the number b.
The maximum possible error in B is known to be 0.005.
Give an example of possible values for B and b such that B is not correct to 2 decimal places.

Give a further example to show that B may not be correct to the nearest integer.

Fixed point iteration

ACTIVITY 2.1 Set your calculator to radian mode.
Key in any number and obtain the cosine.
Now find the cosine of the number displayed.
Continue in this way for some time.

What happens?

The process in Activity 2.1 is described in the diagram in figure 2.11.

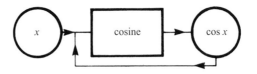

Figure 2.11

You should find that the value displayed becomes closer and closer to 0.739 085 133. What is the significance of this number?

Suppose that you call the number first entered into the calculator x_0. Taking the cosine of this number gives a value x_1 with $x_1 = \cos x_0$. This process is repeated, generating a sequence of numbers $x_0, x_1, x_2, \dots$.

This sequence can be described by the formula $x_{r+1} = \cos x_r$, where x_0 is the number you first keyed into your calculator, for $r = 0, 1, 2, \ldots$. Each term in the sequence is calculated by taking the cosine of the previous term. A formula of this type is called a *recurrence relation*.

In general, in a computational procedure where an operation is repeated, each instance of the repetition is called an *iteration*.

You found in Activity 2.1 that x_r approaches $0.739\,085\,133 \ldots$ as r gets larger and larger. In mathematics it is usual to write

$$x_r \to 0.739\,085\,133 \ldots \text{ as } r \to \infty$$

when this happens and to say x tends to $0.739\,085\,133\ldots$ as r tends to infinity. The number to which the sequence tends (around $0.739\,085\,133$ in this case) is called the *limit* of the sequence.

- This does not happen with all the function keys on a calculator. For example, try using the 'tan' key in place of the 'cos' key in Activity 2.1.

- When the sequence generated does tend towards a limit, the sequence is said to be *convergent* and the number to which the sequence tends is called the *limit* of the sequence.

- In Activity 2.1, after a while, pressing the cosine key makes no difference to the value displayed. Therefore $0.739\,085\,133 \ldots$ must *satisfy* $x = \cos x$, at least to the level of accuracy given by your calculator. So this method has led you to find a good approximation of a root of $x = \cos x$. This equation and this root are illustrated in the graph in figure 2.12.

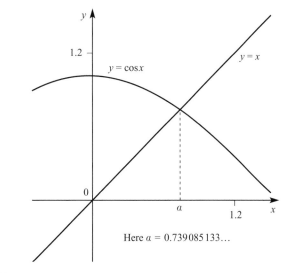

Here $a = 0.739\,085\,133\ldots$

Figure 2.12

This approach can be extended.

- It is possible to rearrange *any* equation into the form $x = g(x)$.

- It may be that the recurrence relation $x_{r+1} = g(x_r)$, where x_0 is given or chosen appropriately, produces a convergent sequence.

- If this is the case, the limit of the sequence will be a root of $x = g(x)$ and therefore it will be a root of the original equation.

A root, a, of the equation $x = g(x)$ is called a *fixed point* of g since evaluating g at a gives a again. In other words, g fixes a. The method described above is called *fixed point iteration*.

Now look at another example of this technique in action.

EXAMPLE 2.3

Show that the equation

$$x^2 - \sin x - 1 = 0$$

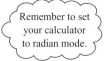

Remember to set your calculator to radian mode.

has a root between 1 and 2.
Show that the equation can be rearranged to

$$x = \sqrt{1 + \sin x}.$$

Use the iteration $x_{r+1} = \sqrt{1 + \sin x_r}$ with $x_0 = 1$ to find this root correct to 4 decimal places.

SOLUTION

Let $f(x) = x^2 - \sin x - 1$.

Since $f(1) = -0.841...$ is negative and $f(2) = 2.090...$ is positive, the equation $x^2 - \sin x - 1 = 0$ has a root between 1 and 2.

The iteration $x_{r+1} = \sqrt{1 + \sin x_r}$ with $x_0 = 1$, gives the values shown in the table.

r	x_r
1	1
2	1.357 008 101
3	1.406 141 602
4	1.409 423 644
5	1.409 612 592
6	1.409 623 354
7	1.409 623 967

$1.357\,008\,101 = \sqrt{1 + \sin 1}$

$1.406\,141\,602 = \sqrt{1 + \sin 1.357\,008\,101}$

The last three values calculated are all 1.4096 to 4 decimal places.
In fact the root, to 4 decimal places, is 1.0496 as $f(1.409\,55) = -0.0002...$ and
$f(1.408\,65) = +0.000\,07...$.

ACTIVITY 2.2

If your calculator has a key labelled 'ANS' it is possible to obtain these values very quickly.

Key 1 into your calculator and press ⊡. This sets the value of 'ANS' to be 1.

Then enter $\sqrt{(1 + \sin \text{ANS})}$ and press ⊡. This should give you the value x_2 from Example 2.3 and also set 'ANS' to be this value.

If you press ⊡ again you should get x_3 and so on.

ACTIVITY 2.3

Show that the equation $x^2 - \sin x - 1 = 0$ can be rearranged into the form $x = g(x)$ where g is any of the following functions.

(i) $g(x) = \arcsin(x^2 - 1)$
(ii) $g(x) = x - (x^2 - \sin x - 1)$
(iii) $g(x) = x - \frac{1}{2}(x^2 - \sin x - 1)$

Use each of these functions to give a recurrence relation $x_{r+1} = g(x_r)$ with $x_0 = 1$ and investigate the sequence obtained in each case.
Remember angles are measured in radians.

EXERCISE 2C

1 Taking $x_0 = 5$ in each case, describe the sequence generated by each of the following recurrence relations.

(i) $x_{r+1} = \tan x_r$
(ii) $x_{r+1} = \sqrt{x_r + 1}$
(iii) $x_{r+1} = \sqrt[3]{x_r}$
(iv) $x_{r+1} = \arcsin\left(\frac{x_r}{5}\right)$

> Obtain the terms of the sequence on your calculator using the method described in Activity 2.2.

2 Show that the equation $x^2 - 4x - 1 = 0$ can be rearranged to give $x = \sqrt{4x + 1}$.

Taking $x_0 = 1$, use your calculator or a spreadsheet program to find the sequence generated by the recurrence relation $x_{r+1} = \sqrt{4x_r + 1}$.

Keep finding terms in this sequence until the value given by your calculator or computer does not change.

Round this value to 5 decimal places.
Check that this value is a root of $x^2 - 4x - 1 = 0$ correct to 5 decimal places.

3 (i) Show that the equation $x^3 + 2x - 1 = 0$ can be rearranged to give $x = \frac{1 - x^3}{2}$.

Taking $x_0 = 0$, use your calculator or a spreadsheet program to find the sequence generated by the recurrence relation $x_{r+1} = \frac{1 - x_r^3}{2}$.

Keep finding terms in this sequence until the value given by your calculator or computer does not change.

Round this value to 5 decimal places.
Check that this value is a root of $x^3 + 2x - 1 = 0$ correct to 5 decimal places.

(ii) Now show that the equation $x^3 + 2x - 1 = 0$ can be rearranged to give
$$x = \sqrt[3]{1 - 2x}.$$

Taking $x_0 = 0$, use your calculator or a spreadsheet program to find the sequence generated by the recurrence relation $x_{r+1} = \sqrt[3]{1 - 2x_r}$.
What happens?

4 In each case below, show that the second equation is a rearrangement of the first.

Use the sequence generated by the recurrence relation suggested by the second equation with $x_0 = 2$ to give a root of the equation correct to 3 decimal places in cases where the resultant sequence converges.

(i) $x^3 - 1 = x^2$, $\qquad x = \sqrt[3]{x^2 + 1}$

(ii) $x^2 + x = 1$, $\qquad x = \dfrac{1}{x + 1}$

(iii) $x^3 - 2x = x^2 + 1$, $\qquad x = \dfrac{x^3 - x^2 - 1}{2}$

(iv) $\sin x - \cos x = 0$ $\qquad x = \arcsin(\cos x)$

Explaining fixed point iteration

Think again about the example of the recurrence relation $x_{r+1} = \cos x_r$ that you first looked at earlier in this chapter. You saw that, with any value of x_0, the sequence produced converges to $0.739\,085\,133\ldots$ which is a root of the equation $x = \cos x$.

Often in mathematics, a graphical representation of a process helps you to understand it. Figure 2.13 shows the graph of $y = \cos x$ and $y = x$.

As discussed previously, the x co-ordinate of any point of intersection is a root of the equation $x = \cos x$. In figure 2.13, such a value is labelled on the x axis as α.

The starting value is called x_0, the next value is x_1, the next x_2 and so on. In figure 2.13, $x_0 = 1$.

The steps taken to form such a diagram for the general recurrence relation $x_{r+1} = g(x_r)$ are as follows.

- Draw a graph with the line $y = x$ and the curve $y = g(x)$ and mark the point at which they cross. You are trying to approximate the x co-ordinate of this point.

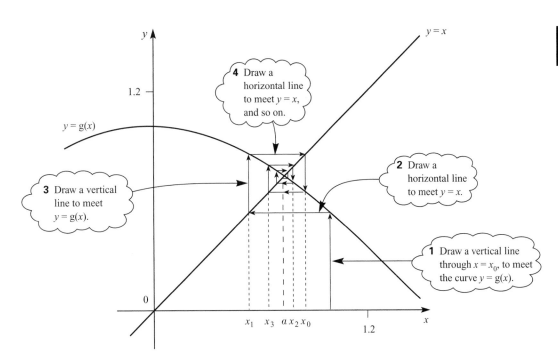

Figure 2.13

- **1** Starting with your initial estimate of x_0 draw the vertical line through $x = x_0$, to meet the curve $y = g(x)$.

  2 From this point, draw a horizontal line to meet $y = x$.

  3 From this point, draw a vertical line to meet $y = g(x)$.

  4 From this point, draw a horizontal line to meet $y = x$ and so on.

  Notice how the line $y = x$ is used to transfer the value of x_1 on the y axis to the x axis so that it can be 'input' into g again to find x_2.

  Figure 2.13 shows how, in this case, subsequent iterations get closer to the root of the equation. It also shows that consecutive iterations are on either side of the root of the equation.

  The diagram in figure 2.13 is an example of a *cobweb diagram*, so-called for obvious reasons.

ACTIVITY 2.4 Key any number between 0 and 1 into your calculator and find its square root. Now obtain the square root of the number displayed and continue in this way for some time.

What happens?

What happens if you repeat the above but taking a starting value greater than 1?

You should find that in both cases, after a while, the display reads 1 and pressing the square root key makes no difference to the value displayed. Therefore 1 must satisfy $x = \sqrt{x}$ (it clearly does). So this method has led you to find a root of $x = \sqrt{x}$.

In this case you would write $x_r \to 1$ as $r \to \infty$, and say x_r tends to 1 as r tends to infinity.

⚠ The symbol $\sqrt{x}$ means the positive square root of x.

If you draw a diagram similar to the one in figure 2.13 and carry out the same construction you should see something like the one shown in figure 2.14. Here x_0 is 0.4.

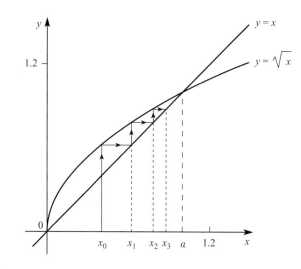

Figure 2.14

You can see from figure 2.14 that the sequence $x_0, x_1, x_2, x_3, \ldots$ generated by the recurrence relation is tending towards the root $a = 1$ of the equation $x = \sqrt{x}$. This time the diagram is referred to as a *staircase diagram*, again for obvious reasons.

In the next activity the behaviour of the sequence is quite different.

ACTIVITY 2.5   Key any number between 1 and 2 into your calculator and square it.
Now obtain the square of the number displayed and continue in this way for some time.

What happens?

You should find that the numbers get larger and larger. Eventually they get so large that your calculator displays an error! So this certainly has not lead you to find a root of $x = x^2$.

Figure 2.15 shows you what is happening.

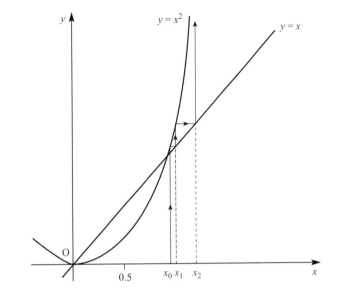

Figure 2.15

❓ How can you find that the roots of the equation $x = 1 - 6x^2$ are $x = \frac{1}{3}$ and $x = -\frac{1}{2}$?

Let $x_0 = 0.4$. Find $x_1 = 1 - 6x_0^2$. Then find $x_2 = 1 - 6x_1^2$ and so on.

What happens?

Once again the sequence does not tend towards a root of $x = 1 - 6x^2$.

Figure 2.16 explains this.

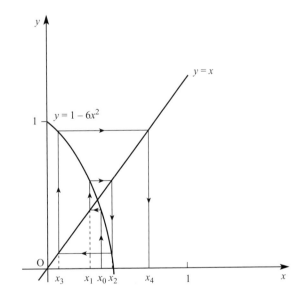

Figure 2.16

You may have noticed that, with an appropriate starting value,

- a cobweb results when $y = g(x)$ has a negative gradient at its point of intersection with $y = x$.

Moreover if the gradient of $g(x)$ at this point is between -1 and 0, then the cobweb is contracting and so the iterations converge to the corresponding solution of $x = g(x)$. See figure 2.17.

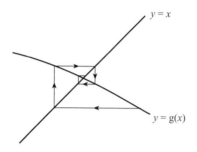

Figure 2.17

- If the gradient of $g(x)$ at this point is less than -1, then the cobweb is expanding and so the iterations do not converge. See figure 2.18.

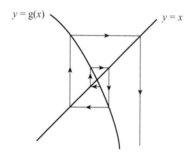

Figure 2.18

- A staircase will result when $y = g(x)$ has a positive gradient at its point of intersection with $y = x$. Moreover if the gradient of $g(x)$ at this point is less than 1, then the staircase leads towards the point and so the iterations converge to the corresponding root of $x = g(x)$. See figure 2.19.

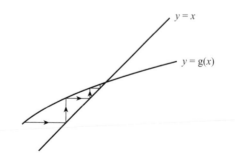

Figure 2.19

- If the gradient of g(x) at this point is greater than 1, then the staircase leads away from the point and so the iterations do not converge to the corresponding root of $x = g(x)$. See figure 2.20.

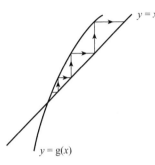

$y = x$

$y = g(x)$

Figure 2.20

The conditions which ensure a sequence converges can be summarised as follows.

If a is a fixed point of the function g and the gradient of g at a is between -1 and 1 and x_0 is sufficiently close to a then the sequence generated by $x_{r+1} = g(x_r)$ will converge to the value a.

This will be explored in more detail in Chapter 6.

EXAMPLE 2.4

The equation $x^3 - x^2 - 1 = 0$ has a root near to $x = 1.5$.

(i) Show that the equation can be rearranged to give $x = x^2 - \dfrac{1}{x}$ (if $x \neq 0$).

(ii) Describe the sequence given by the iteration $x_{r+1} = x_r^2 - \dfrac{1}{x_r}$ with the starting value $x_0 = 1.5$.

(iii) Explain its behaviour in terms of the derivative of $g(x) = x^2 - \dfrac{1}{x}$ near to the root.

SOLUTION

(i) $x^3 - x^2 - 1 = 0 \implies x^2 = x^3 - 1 \implies x = x^2 - \dfrac{1}{x}$ (if $x \neq 0$).

(ii) Let $x_0 = 1.5$.

The iteration $x_{r+1} = x_r^2 - \dfrac{1}{x_r}$ gives

$$x_1 = x_0^2 - \frac{1}{x_0} = 1.5^2 - \frac{1}{1.5} = 1.583\,333.$$

Continuing this gives the values shown in the table.

r	0	1	2	3	4	5	6
x_r	1.5	1.583 333	1.875 365	2.983 766	8.567 715	73.289 02	5371.267

The iterations are increasing and moving away from the root.

(iii) Since $g(x) = x^2 - \dfrac{1}{x}$, $g'(x) = 2x + \dfrac{1}{x^2}$ and $g'(1.5) = 3 + \dfrac{1}{2.25} = 3.44$.

The fact that $g'(1.5)$ is greater than 1 explains the series of estimates increasing and moving away from the root. The situation is similar to that shown in figure 2.20.

❓ Explain why, when an iteration produces a contracting spiral, the iterations themselves can be used to produce interval estimates to the root.

---

1 Show that the equation $0.5 \sin x - x + 3 = 0$ has a root between 0 radians and 2π radians.

Use the iteration $x_{r+1} = 0.5 \sin x_r + 3$ with $x_0 = 2.5$ to find the solution correct to 2 decimal places.

2 (i) Show that, if either of the following iterative formulae converge, they will converge to a root of the equation $x^2 - 6x + 5 = 0$. (Do not actually carry out any of the iterations, just show this algebraically.)

(a) $x_{r+1} = 6 - \dfrac{5}{x_r}$ **(b)** $x_{r+1} = \dfrac{x_r^2 + 5}{6}$

(ii) What are the two roots of this equation?

(iii) By considering the gradient of the recurrence relation formula, in each case determine whether or not the formula will converge to either root of $x^2 - 6x + 5 = 0$, assuming that a suitable starting value is chosen.

(iv) Confirm that your findings are true by carrying out iterations with suitable starting values.

3 Show that the sequences defined by

(i) $x_{r+1} = \tfrac{1}{3}(x_r^2 + 2)$ **(ii)** $x_{r+1} = 3 - \dfrac{2}{x_r}$

with suitable starting values will converge to different roots of the same equation. In each case construct cobweb or staircase diagrams to show the behaviour near the roots.

4 (i) Examine the terms of the sequences obtained from $x_{r+1} = x_r + \dfrac{1}{x_r^3}$ with $x_0 = 1, 4, 5, 10$ and 20.

(ii) Let $g(x) = x = + \dfrac{1}{x^3}$ and, by examining the graphs of $y = x$ and $y = g(x)$, explain the results you obtained in part **(i)**.

5 The equation $100x = 101 \cos x$ is to be solved numerically.

(i) Show, graphically or otherwise, that the equation has a root between 0.7 and 0.8.

(ii) Use the iteration $x_{r+1} = 1.01 \cos x_r$ to find this root correct to 3 decimal places.

The Newton–Raphson method

The curve in figure 2.21 is a graph of $f(x) = x^2 - 2$. The x co-ordinate of the point where this curve crosses the x axis, labeled a, is a root of $x^2 - 2 = 0$. From the diagram it seems that a reasonable initial approximation to a may be $x_0 = 2$.

The straight line shown is the tangent to $f(x) = x^2 - 2$ at the point $(2, 2)$. The point, x_1, where this line crosses the x axis looks as though it is much closer to a.

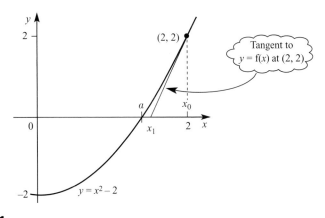

Figure 2.21

x_1 can be calculated as follows.

- To find the equation of the tangent at $(2, 2)$, find the gradient of $f(x) = x^2 - 2$ at $(2, 2)$. Differentiating gives $f'(x) = 2x$ and so $f'(2) = 4$; the gradient is 4.

- So the tangent is $y - 2 = 4(x - 2)$ or $y = 4x - 6$.

- This crosses the x axis when $y = 0$ and so $x_1 = \frac{6}{4} = 1.5$.

You can now repeat this procedure by finding the point where the tangent to $y = f(x)$ when $x = 1.5$ crosses the x axis. This is the idea behind the Newton–Raphson method.

❓ Show that this gives 1.4166... as a next approximation.
What is the next approximation after that?

The task of calculating the equation of the tangent at each step soon becomes tedious. What is required is a formula which gives the new approximation in terms of the old one.

Figure 2.22 shows the graph of a general function $f(x)$. The equation $f(x) = 0$ has a root at $x = a$.

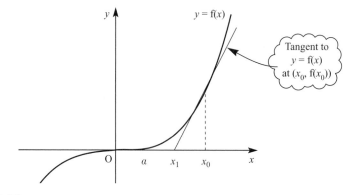

Figure 2.22

In the Newton–Raphson method, a guess, x_0, is taken to the root as shown.

Then, x_1 in the diagram is taken as the new, better approximation of the root.

So the question is 'If you know the function, f, and the point x_0, how do you calculate x_1?'

? The tangent is a straight line and so it has an equation of the form $y = mx + c$.

(i) Why must $m = f'(x_0)$?

(ii) You can find c by using the fact that the line goes through the point $(x_0, f(x_0))$. Show that $c = f(x_0) - f'(x_0)x_0$.

(iii) So the equation of the tangent is

$$y = f'(x_0)x + (f(x_0) - f'(x_0)x_0)$$

and x_1 is the point at which this line crosses the x axis.

Show that $x_1 = x_0 - \dfrac{f(x_0)}{f'(x_0)}$ (if $f'(x_0) \neq 0$).

This can be repeated to find an even better approximation, usually called x_2. The relationship between x_1 and x_2 is the same as the relationship between x_0 and x_1. So

$$x_2 = x_1 - \frac{f(x_1)}{f'(x_1)}.$$

Hence the iterative formula is

$$x_{r+1} = x_r - \frac{f(x_r)}{f'(x_r)}.$$

Notice that the original intention was to find a formula for x_1 from x_0. The formula above is much better than that as it is an iterative formula setting up the whole process.

Historical note

The method was devised by Isaac Newton in the seventeenth century and first published by his student Joseph Raphson in 1690. Newton's contribution to science is among the greatest of all time; mathematics was only one area in which he worked and his great rival in that field, Leibniz, said of him 'Taking mathematics from the beginning of the world to the time of Newton, what he has done is much the better half'. He was a stimulus to many in the following century and yet, at the end of his life he stated 'I do not know what I may appear to the world; but to myself I seem to have been only like a boy playing on the seashore, and diverting myself in now and then finding a smoother pebble or a prettier shell than ordinary, whilst the great ocean of truth lay all undiscovered before me'.

EXAMPLE 2.5

Use the Newton–Raphson method to find the root of the equation $x^4 + x - 3 = 0$ near $x = 1.5$.

With $x_0 = 1.5$, use the method three times (in other words calculate as far as x_4). Hence, give an approximation to the root and state its accuracy.

SOLUTION

The iterative formula in the case of $f(x) = x^4 + x - 3$ is as follows.

$$x_{r+1} = x_r - \frac{f(x_r)}{f'(x_r)}$$

$$= x_r - \left(\frac{x_r^4 + x_r - 3}{4x_r^3 + 1} \right)$$

Thus $x_1 = x_0 - \left(\frac{x_0^4 + x_0 - 3}{4x_0^3 + 1} \right)$

$$= 1.5 - \left(\frac{1.5^4 + 1.5 - 3}{(4 \times 1.5^3) + 1} \right)$$

$$= 1.254\,310$$

Similarly $x_2 = x_1 - \left(\frac{x_1^4 + x_1 - 3}{4x_1^3 + 1} \right)$

$$= 1.172\,278,$$

$x_3 = 1.164\,110$ and $x_4 = 1.164\,035$.

From this evidence it looks as though 1.164 may be an estimate to the root which is correct to 3 decimal places.

You can check this by verifying that the function changes sign between 1.1635 and 1.1645. In fact $f(1.1635) = -0.003\,91 < 0$ and $f(1.1645) = 0.003\,339 > 0$.

It is possible to get the values $x_1, x_2, x_3, \ldots$ very quickly using a suitable calculator. For this example, if your calculator has a key labelled 'ANS' then type 1.5 followed by $\boxed{=}$. Then type ANS – ((ANS^4 + ANS – 3) ÷ (4ANS^3 + 1)). Pressing $\boxed{=}$ repeatedly will then give you subsequent iterations.

For most functions you will see that with an appropriate starting value, x_0, the sequence $x_1, x_2, x_3, \ldots$ generated using this method quickly approaches a root of $f(x) = 0$. The rate at which such a sequence gets close to the root is considered in the next investigation and is discussed further in Chapter 6.

ACTIVITY 2.5

1 By applying the Newton–Raphson method to the equation $x^2 - 7 = 0$ derive an iterative formula for approximating $\sqrt{7}$.

2 Use it, with $x_0 = 3$, to obtain an approximation of $\sqrt{7}$ which is correct to as many decimal places as you can.

3 Using this approximation as the exact value, calculate the absolute error in each of the values x_0, x_1, x_2, x_3, x_4.

4 Comment on the rate at which the sequence $x_0, x_1, x_2, \ldots$ approaches $\sqrt{7}$.

The secant method

In most cases the Newton–Raphson method works very well, but a difficulty that can arise is finding $f'(x)$. This can be particularly problematic when using a computer to carry out the iterations as differentiation is not a natural process for a computer to perform.

This difficulty can be overcome by approximating the derivative. If you have two approximations x_0 and x_1 to the root of an equation $f(x) = 0$ as shown in figure 2.23, you could use the gradient of the line joining $A(x_0, f(x_0))$ and $B(x_1, f(x_1))$ as an approximation to the gradient of the tangent at B.

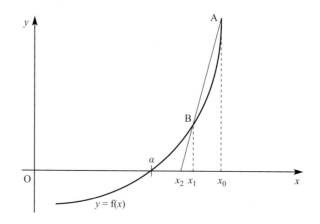

Figure 2.23

In practice this means using the value x_2 shown in figure 2.23 as an improved approximation to the root a.

It turns out that $x_2 = \dfrac{x_0 f(x_1) - x_1 f(x_0)}{f(x_1) - f(x_0)}$. This formula is derived below. You need to be careful with the algebra!

In figure 2.23 the gradient of the line AB is $\dfrac{f(x_1) - f(x_0)}{x_1 - x_0}$. You can use this as an approximation to the derivative $f'(x_1)$ in the Newton–Raphson method to produce the next improved approximation. In other words, replace $f'(x_1)$ in the formula $x_2 = x_1 - \dfrac{f(x_1)}{f'(x_1)}$ with $\dfrac{f(x_1) - f(x_0)}{x_1 - x_0}$.

$$x_2 = x_1 - \frac{f(x_1)}{\left(\dfrac{f(x_1) - f(x_0)}{x_1 - x_0}\right)}$$

$$= x_1 - \left(\frac{x_1 - x_0}{f(x_1) - f(x_0)}\right)f(x_1)$$

$$= \frac{x_1(f(x_1) - f(x_0)) - (x_1 - x_0)f(x_1)}{f(x_1) - f(x_0)}$$

$$= \frac{x_0 f(x_1) - x_1 f(x_0)}{f(x_1) - f(x_0)}$$

 Explain each step in the algebra above.

You can then go on to use x_1 and x_2 to calculate a new estimate x_3, then x_2 and x_3 to give x_4 and so on. In general x_{r+1} in terms of x_r and x_{r-1} is given by

$$x_{r+1} = \frac{x_{r-1}f(x_r) - x_r f(x_{r-1})}{f(x_r) - f(x_{r-1})}.$$

This is called the *secant method*.

EXAMPLE 2.6   Figure 2.24 shows a graph of $f(x) = 4x^3 - 5x + 1$.

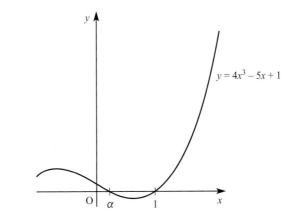

$y = 4x^3 - 5x + 1$

Figure 2.24

(i) Use the secant method with starting values of $x_0 = -0.5$ and $x_1 = 0$ to give an approximation, correct to 3 decimal places, to the root of $4x^3 - 5x + 1 = 0$ labeled a.

Draw a diagram to illustrate the first three iterations.

(ii) Compare the sequence obtained using the secant method to the sequence obtained using the Newton–Raphson method with a starting value of zero.

SOLUTION

(i) Using the formula,

$$x_2 = \frac{x_0 f(x_1) - x_1 f(x_0)}{f(x_1) - f(x_0)}$$

$$= \frac{0 \times f(-0.5) - (-0.5) \times f(0)}{f(-0.5) - f(0)}$$

$$= 0.25.$$

Then

$$x_3 = \frac{x_1 f(x_2) - x_2 f(x_1)}{f(x_2) - f(x_1)}$$

$$= \frac{(-0.5) \times f(0.25) - 0.25 \times f(-0.5)}{f(0.25) - f(-0.5)}$$

$$= 0.210\,526\,316$$

and so on giving the following values of x_0, x_1, x_2, x_3, x_4, x_5 and x_6.

r	0	1	2	3	4	5	6
x_r	−0.5	0	0.25	0.210 526 316	0.207 016 987	0.207 106 953	0.207 106 781

The last four estimates agree to 3 decimal places, they all round to 0.207. A sign-change check shows that 0.207 is an approximation of the root correct to 3 decimal places.

Figure 2.25 shows the first three iterations.

(ii) The iterative formula for the Newton–Raphson method is

$$x_{r+1} = x_r - \frac{f(x_r)}{f'(x_r)}$$

$$= x_r - \left(\frac{4x_r^3 - 5x_r + 1}{12x_r^2 - 5} \right).$$

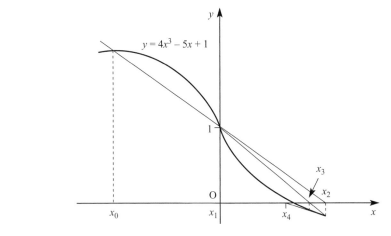

Figure 2.25

Taking the starting value $x_1 = 0$ this gives the following values.

r	1	2	3	4	5	6
x_r	0	0.2	0.207 079 646	0.207 106 781	0.207 106 781	0.207 106 781

These are quite similar to the ones obtained from the secant method given in part **(i)** and roughly the same number of iterations are required to obtain the same degree of accuracy.

1 Use the Newton–Raphson method, with $x_0 = 1.5$, to find a root of $x^4 - x^2 - 2 = 0$ correct to 5 decimal places.
Use a sign-change argument to check your claim.

2 Use the Newton–Raphson method, with the starting values given, to solve the following equations correct to 5 decimal places.
Verify that your solution has the desired degree of accuracy in each case.
   (i) $x^4 = 3 - x$, $\quad x_0 = 1.5$
   (ii) $x^4 - 2 = 0$, $\quad x_0 = 1.5$
   (iii) $x^5 + 3x = 2 - x^4$, $\quad x_0 = 1$
   (iv) $x + \sqrt{x} = 1$, $\quad x_0 = 1$

3 Consider the equation $(x-1)^3(x-2) = 0$. This clearly has solutions of $x = 1$ and $x = 2$.
For the following starting values, $x_0 = 0.5$, 1.5 and 2.5, calculate the first four iterations using the Newton–Raphson method and comment on the results.

4 Obtain the value of $\sqrt[3]{25}$ correct to 6 decimal places using both the bisection method and the Newton–Raphson method.
Note the contrast in the number of iterations required in each case.

5 The equation $x^3 - 9x^2 + 6 = 0$ has a root, a, in the interval $(0, 1)$.
Use the Newton–Raphson method, starting with $x_0 = 0.8$, to find a correct to
7 decimal places.
(You are advised to work with as many decimal places as your calculator
supports.)

[MEI, *part*]

6 The iterative formula $x_{r+1} = 0.8(1 - x_r^3)$ is used with starting values of
  (a) $x_0 = 1.3$
  (b) $x_0 = 0.6$.

  (i) Describe in each case how the sequence of iterates behaves.
  (ii) The equation $x = 0.8(1 - x^3)$ has only one real root, a.
      Use your answer to part **(i)** to determine a correct to 5 significant figures.
  (iii) Evaluate $f'(a)$ where $f(x) = 0.8(1 - x^3)$ using your answer to part **(ii)**.
      Explain how this value relates to the behaviour of the iteration in part **(i)** **(b)**.

[MEI, *adapted*]

7 Use the secant method to solve the following four equations correct to
5 decimal places. The starting values are given in each case.
  (i) $x^4 = 3 - x$, $x_0 = 1.5, x_1 = 1.3$
  (ii) $x^4 - 2 = 0$, $x_0 = 1.5, x_1 = 1.3$
  (iii) $\cos x - 0.6x = 0$, $x_0 = 1.1$ radians, $x_1 = 1$ radians
  (iv) $2\cos x = 1 - 5x$, $x_0 = 0$ radians, $x_1 = -0.1$ radians

8 Use the secant method with $x_0 = 0.5$ radians and $x_1 = 0.7$ radians to
approximate the smaller positive root of $\sin x - \cos 2x - 1 = 0$ correct to
5 decimal places.

9 The diagram shows the graph of $y = f(x)$ and a root, a, of the equation $f(x) = 0$.
It also shows x_0 and x_1 which are two estimates of a.

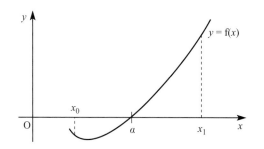

  (i) Copy the diagram, and then use your copy to illustrate the secant method
      for the solution of the equation $f(x) = 0$.
      You should show the positions of the next four estimates, x_2, x_3, x_4 and x_5.
  (ii) Show that the equation $3\sin x - x = 0$ (where the angle is in radians) has a
      root in the interval $(2, 3)$.

      Find the root, correct to 4 decimal places, using the secant method.

[MEI, *part*]

The method of false position

Figure 2.26 shows a graph of $f(x) = x^2 + x - 3$. A root of the equation $f(x) = 0$ between $x = 1$ and $x = 2$ is labelled a in the diagram. The points $(1, -1)$ and $(2, 3)$ on the graph are labelled A and B respectively.

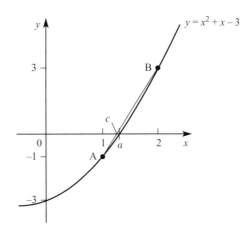

Figure 2.26

It looks as though, c, where the line AB crosses the x axis is a good approximation to the root a.

One way to calculate c is to find the equation of the straight line AB and then use it to find where it crosses the x axis.

The gradient of AB is

$$\frac{\text{change in } y \text{ co-ordinates}}{\text{change in } x \text{ co-ordinates}} = \frac{3 - (-1)}{2 - 1} = 4.$$

The co-ordinates of B are $(2, 3)$ and so the equation of AB is

$$y - 3 = 4(x - 2).$$

This line crosses the x axis when $y = 0$ so $c = \frac{5}{4} = 1.25$.

You can take this further. By checking the sign of $f(1.25)$ you can find out whether the root is between $x = 1$ and $x = 1.25$ or between $x = 1.25$ and $x = 2$. It is clear from figure 2.26 that in this case it is the latter. In fact $f(1.25) = -0.1875$.

Then you can work out where the line between $(1.25, -0.1875)$ and $(2, 3)$ cuts the x axis to get an improved approximation.

Continuing in this way, a sequence of approximations can be obtained.

The task of finding the new approximation at each step soon becomes tedious. It would be advantageous to have a general formula which gives the new approximation in terms of the two points straddling the root.

Figure 2.27 shows two points, *a* and *b*, which straddle a root, *a*, of f(*x*) = 0.

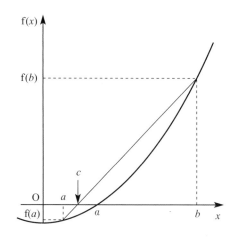

Figure 2.27

Your first approximation of *a* will be the value *c* shown in the diagram.

This is the *x* co-ordinate of the point where the straight line joining the point (*a*, f(*a*)) to the point (*b*, f(*b*)) crosses the *x* axis.

The formula for *c* is

$$c = \frac{a\mathrm{f}(b) - b\mathrm{f}(a)}{\mathrm{f}(b) - \mathrm{f}(a)}.$$

You can work out this formula as follows. There are two triangles in figure 2.27 (make sure you can spot them) and they are similar.
The triangles have been redrawn in figure 2.28 and the lengths of some of the sides have been labelled.

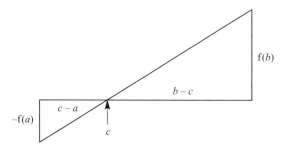

Figure 2.28

? **(i)** Why is one of the lengths –f(*a*) and not f(*a*)?

(ii) Explain why $\dfrac{\mathrm{f}(b)}{-\mathrm{f}(a)} = \dfrac{b-c}{c-a}$.

(iii) The expression in part **(ii)** can be rearranged to give a formula for *c*, as follows.

Explain each of the steps below.

$$\frac{f(b)}{-f(a)} = \frac{b-c}{c-a}$$

$\Rightarrow \qquad f(b)(c-a) = -f(a)(b-c)$

$\Rightarrow \qquad f(b)c - f(b)a = f(a)c - f(a)b$

$\Rightarrow \qquad f(b)c - f(a)c = af(b) - bf(a)$

$\Rightarrow \qquad (f(b) - f(a))c = af(b) - bf(a)$

$$c = \frac{af(b) - bf(a)}{f(b) - f(a)}$$

Once c has been calculated, a better approximation can be calculated by repeating this taking whichever of a and c or c and b are two points straddling the root as a starting point. The example below illustrates the use of the method of false position.

EXAMPLE 2.7

Show that the equation $f(x) = x^2 - 7 = 0$ has a root, a, between 2 and 3. By using the method of false position, starting with these two values, find an estimate to this root which is correct to 5 decimal places.

SOLUTION

Since $f(2) = -5 < 0$ and $f(3) = 2 > 0$ the function must cross the x axis between $x = 2$ and $x = 3$ and so there will be a root of $f(x) = 0$ there.

With $a = 2$ and $b = 3$, the method of false position gives a first approximation to the solution of

$$x_1 = c = \frac{af(b) - bf(a)}{f(b) - f(a)}$$

$$= \frac{(2 \times f(3)) - (3 \times f(2))}{f(3) - f(2)}$$

$$= \frac{(2 \times 2) - (3 \times -3)}{2 - (-3)}$$

$$= \frac{13}{5}$$

$$= 2.6.$$

Since $f(2.6) = -0.24$ the points 2.6 and 3 straddle the solution.

Therefore $2.6 < a < 3$ and you can apply the procedure again by calculating $x_2 = c = \dfrac{af(b) - bf(a)}{f(b) - f(a)}$ with $a = 2.6$ and $b = 3$.

The results of doing this and further repetitions are shown in the table.

r	Value of a	Sign of $f(a)$	Value of b	Sign of $f(b)$	Value of x_r	Sign $f(x_r)$
1	2.000 000 000	<0	3.000 000 000	>0	2.600 000 000	<0
2	2.600 000 000	<0	3.000 000 000	>0	2.642 857 143	<0
3	2.642 857 143	<0	3.000 000 000	>0	2.645 569 620	<0
4	2.645 569 620	<0	3.000 000 000	>0	2.645 739 910	<0
5	2.645 739 910	<0	3.000 000 000	>0	2.645 750 596	<0
6	2.645 750 596	<0	3.000 000 000	>0	2.645 751 266	<0
7	2.645 751 266	<0	3.000 000 000	>0	2.645 751 308	<0

So a sequence of estimates to the root is as follows.

$x_1 = 2.6$

$x_2 = 2.642\,857\,143$

$x_3 = 2.645\,569\,620$

$x_4 = 2.645\,739\,910$

$x_5 = 2.645\,750\,596$

$x_6 = 2.645\,751\,266$

$x_7 = 2.645\,751\,308$

These can be used in the usual way to give an approximation to the root correct to a number of decimal places.
It can be shown using a sign-change check that 2.645 75 is correct to 5 decimal places.

 In the table in Example 2.7, the value of b never changes, whereas the value of a gets closer and closer to the root of $x^2 - 7 = 0$ from the left.
Explain this in terms of the graph of $f(x) = x^2 - 7$.

In the next activity you look at the behaviour of the error in approximations given by the method of false position.

ACTIVITY 2.6

A root of the equation $x^2 - \sin x - 1 = 0$ lies between $x = 1$ radian and $x = 2$ radians.

1 Carry out eight iterations of the method of false position and hence write down an approximation of the root which is correct to as many decimal places as it is possible to deduce from your results.

2 Taking this value to be the exact value of the root, as this is the best approximation that is available, work out the absolute error in each of the approximations obtained.

EXERCISE 2F

1 Use a graphical calculator to sketch each of the functions below. Hence, for each function, find two values which straddle a root of $f(x) = 0$. Beginning with these two values, use the method of false position to determine the root correct to 3 decimal places.

(i) $f(x) = x^3 + 7x - 9$

(ii) $f(x) = \sqrt{x} - \cos 0.5x$

(iii) $f(x) = x^7 + x^3 - 1$

(iv) $f(x) = x^4 - 3.2x^3 - 1.7x + 2.4$

Remember angles are measured in radians.

2 Use the method of false position to find a root of each of the following equations with an error of less than 0.05 in each case. A graph will help you to identify suitable starting values.

(i) $x^2 = 3(x + 1)$

(ii) $x = \cos x$

(iii) $x^2 = \sin x + 1$

3 It is given that $f(x) = mx + c$ is a linear function (with $m \neq 0$).

☆ Show, using a diagram, that if the method of false position is used to find the
☆ root of $f(x) = 0$ then the first approximation given is the exact value of the root.
☆ (Challenge: Try to prove this algebraically.)

1 You can attempt to solve any equation numerically.

An equation of the form $r(x) = s(x)$ (for example, $\cos x = x^2 + x^3$) may need to be rearranged.

The methods in this chapter use the forms $f(x) = 0$ (for example, $\cos x - x^2 - x^3 = 0$) and $x = g(x)$ (for example, $x = \sqrt{\cos x - x^3}$).

2 **The method of bisection**

If a root of an equation $f(x) = 0$ lies between a and b, then $c = \dfrac{a+b}{2}$ gives an approximation to the root.

You can then determine whether the root lies between a and c or between b and c and repeat this idea, obtaining better and better interval estimates to the root.

Eventually you can give an approximation of the root to the desired degree of accuracy.

3 **Fixed point iteration**

The value α is called a fixed point of the function g if $\alpha = g(\alpha)$.

If α is a fixed point of the function g and the gradient of g at α is between -1 and 1 and x_0 is sufficiently close to α

then the sequence generated by $x_{r+1} = g(x_r)$ will converge to the value α.

4 **The Newton–Raphson method**

The sequence of values generated by

$$x_{r+1} = x_r - \frac{f(x_r)}{f'(x_r)}$$

with x_0 an appropriate estimate, usually converges to a root of $f(x) = 0$ near to x_0.

5 **The secant method**

If x_0 and x_1 are approximations of a root of $f(x) = 0$, the sequence of values generated by

$$x_{r+1} = \frac{x_{r-1}f(x_r) - x_r f(x_{r-1})}{f(x_r) - f(x_{r-1})}$$

usually converges to a root of $f(x) = 0$.

6 **The method of false position**

If a root of an equation $f(x) = 0$ lies between a and b, then

$$c = \frac{af(b) - bf(a)}{f(b) - f(a)}$$

gives an approximation of the root. You then determine whether the root lies between a and c or between b and c and repeat this process to obtain a sequence of approximations to the root.

Numerical integration

It is the glory of geometry that from so few principles, fetched from without, it is able to accomplish so much.

Isaac Newton

In the design of buildings and manufactured goods, irregular shapes are often used for aesthetic or practical reasons. Since properties of these shapes such as the length of a curve, an area or a volume, may be required, you must look for mathematical techniques which can be used to calculate them. To illustrate such a technique, think about the following problem regarding the construction of a patio.

In a sunny garden, it is decided that a patio should be constructed in a sheltered corner by the house. An architect produces the design shown in figure 3.1.

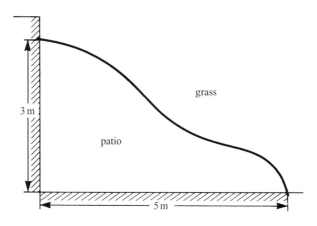

Figure 3.1

The patio is to be covered in concrete up to a depth of 80 mm, the concrete being supplied already mixed. The problem is to estimate the volume of concrete which should be ordered. Since the volume is given by the product of the area of the patio and the depth of the concrete, the problem reduces to one of finding the area of the patio.

The area is given by $\int_0^5 f(x)dx$, where the curve is given by $y = f(x)$. The problem is that often you do not know $f(x)$, or you know it but cannot do the integration.

An alternative approach to this problem is to subdivide the area into regular shapes, for example rectangles or triangles which approximately cover the area. One of the ways in which this might be done is the basis of the following method.

The mid-point rule

The mid-point rule uses rectangles to approximate the area underneath a curve.

In figure 3.2 four rectangles, each with the same width, are used to approximate the area under the graph of a function $f(x)$ between $x = a$ and $x = b$.

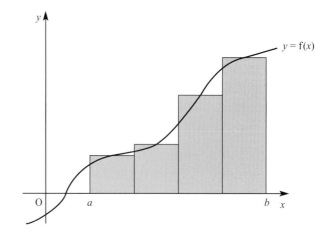

Figure 3.2

The width of each rectangle is h. The height of the first rectangle is the value of the function at the mid-point of the interval from a to $a + h$, i.e. at $a + \dfrac{h}{2}$. This has been labelled m_1 in figure 3.3. The height of this rectangle is $f(m_1)$, its width is h and so its area is $hf(m_1)$.

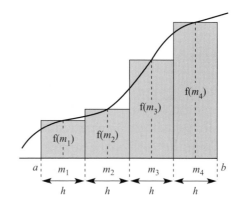

Figure 3.3

The mid-points of the four rectangles are

$$m_1 = a + \frac{h}{2}, \quad m_2 = a + \frac{3h}{2} \quad m_3 = a + \frac{5h}{2} \quad \text{and} \quad m_4 = a + \frac{7h}{2}.$$

The heights of the corresponding rectangles are

$$f(m_1), \quad f(m_2), \quad f(m_3) \quad \text{and} \quad f(m_4).$$

You can see that the total area of the four rectangles in figure 3.2 is

$$hf(m_1) + hf(m_2) + hf(m_3) + hf(m_4) = h[f(m_1) + f(m_2) + f(m_3) + f(m_4)].$$

This particular approximation to $\int_a^b f(x)dx$ is called M_4. This means the mid-point rule approximation with four 'strips'.

You can carry out this procedure with any number of rectangles. Intuitively, you would expect that the more rectangles you use, the closer the value obtained will be to the exact area beneath the curve.

The general form of the mid-point rule, using n strips, each of width h gives the following approximation of $\int_a^b f(x)dx$.

$$M_n = h(f(m_1) + f(m_2) + ... + f(m_n))$$

where $m_1, m_2, ..., m_n$ are the values of x at the mid-points of the strips, and $h = \dfrac{b-a}{n}$.

❓ Why must $h = \dfrac{b-a}{n}$?

As an example, think about calculating the mid-point rule approximations, M_1, M_2, M_4 and M_8, to the area beneath the graph of $f(x) = \cos x$ between $a = 0$ radians and $b = \dfrac{\pi}{2}$ radians.

The value M_1 uses just one rectangle with a base that stretches from $a = 0$ to $b = \dfrac{\pi}{2}$ (see figure 3.4). This has its mid-point at $\dfrac{\pi}{4}$.

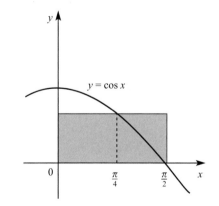

Figure 3.4

Therefore the height of the single rectangle used to estimate the area is

$$f\left(\frac{\pi}{4}\right) = \cos\left(\frac{\pi}{4}\right) = \frac{1}{\sqrt{2}}$$

and its width is $\frac{\pi}{2}$. So

$$M_1 = \frac{1}{\sqrt{2}} \times \frac{\pi}{2}$$

$$= 1.110\,720\,735 \text{ (to 9 d.p.)}.$$

For M_2 you divide the interval into two strips of equal width, $h = \frac{\pi}{4}$. The first of these goes from $a = 0$ to $a + h = \frac{\pi}{4}$ and the second from $a + h = \frac{\pi}{4}$ to $b = a + 2h = \frac{\pi}{2}$ (see figure 3.5). The respective mid-points are at $\frac{\pi}{8}$ and at $\frac{3\pi}{8}$.

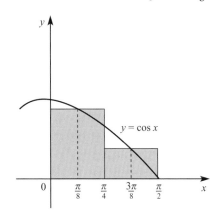

Figure 3.5

Therefore the two rectangles both have width $\frac{\pi}{4}$ and have heights of $f\left(\frac{\pi}{8}\right)$ and $f\left(\frac{3\pi}{8}\right)$ respectively. This gives

$$M_2 = \frac{\pi}{4} \times \left(\cos\left(\frac{\pi}{8}\right) + \cos\left(\frac{3\pi}{8}\right)\right)$$

$$= 1.026\,172\,153 \text{ (to 9 d.p.)}.$$

With four strips, each rectangle has a width of $\frac{\pi}{8}$.

The mid-points of the strips are at $x = \frac{\pi}{16}, \frac{3\pi}{16}, \frac{5\pi}{16}$ and $\frac{7\pi}{16}$. Therefore,

$$M_4 = \frac{\pi}{8} \times \left(\cos\left(\frac{\pi}{16}\right) + \cos\left(\frac{3\pi}{16}\right) + \cos\left(\frac{5\pi}{16}\right) + \cos\left(\frac{7\pi}{16}\right)\right)$$

$$= 1.006\,454\,543 \text{ (to 9 d.p.)}.$$

Finally

$$M_8 = \frac{\pi}{16} \times \left(\cos\left(\frac{\pi}{32}\right) + \cos\left(\frac{3\pi}{32}\right) + \dots + \cos\left(\frac{13\pi}{32}\right) + \cos\left(\frac{15\pi}{32}\right)\right).$$

$$= 1.001\,608\,189 \text{ (to 9 d.p.)}.$$

EXAMPLE 3.1

Use the mid-point rule with five strips to obtain an approximation to

$$\int_0^1 \sqrt{x^3 + 1}\, dx.$$

SOLUTION

Since you are using five strips, and the interval of integration is from 0 to 1, the strip width, h, is $\frac{1}{5}$ or 0.2.

The mid-point of the first strip is at $m_1 = 0.1$; the mid-point of the last strip is at $m_5 = 0.9$.

Figure 3.6

x	0.1	0.3	0.5	0.7	0.9
$\sqrt{x^3 + 1}$	1.000	1.013	1.061	1.159	1.315

The approximation to the integral is

$$0.2 \times (1.000 + 1.013 + 1.061 + 1.159 + 1.315)$$
$$= 0.2 \times 5.548$$
$$= 1.110.$$

Note

The answer has been given to 3 decimal places but you do *not* know that the approximation to the integral is *correct* to 3 decimal places since the mid-point rule only approximates the value of the integral.

ACTIVITY 3.1

1 The mid-point rule is to be used to approximate $\int_1^2 \frac{1}{x^2}\, dx$, using four strips.

Write down the values of m_1, m_2, m_3 and m_4, the mid-points of the sides of the rectangles which lie on the x axis.
Hence determine the approximation to the integral, giving your answer correct to 3 decimal places.

Obtain the exact value of the integral by integration and write down the error in your approximation.

2 Use the mid-point rule to obtain an estimate of the value of the integral

$$\int_0^1 \sqrt{x^3 + 3}\, dx$$

(i) using two strips
(ii) using four strips.

EXERCISE 3A

1 Use the mid-point rule with five strips to estimate the following integrals. Carry as many decimal places as you can in your working.

(i) $\int_0^{0.5} \sqrt{1 + x^3}\, dx$

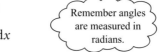

Remember angles are measured in radians.

(ii) $\int_0^1 \cos(1 + x^2)\, dx$

2 (i) Using a calculator or spreadsheet program, find the approximations M_1, M_2 and M_4 to the following integrals to 4 decimal places. Carry as many decimal places as you can in your working.

(a) $\int_0^1 x^2 dx$

(b) $\int_0^{0.5} \sin(x^2)\, dx$

(c) $\int_0^2 (\sin x + \cos x)\, dx$

(ii) Calculate the exact value of the integral in part (i) (a) and then calculate and comment upon the error in each of the approximations you found.

3 A function f has the values given in the following table.

x	1.8	2.0	2.2	2.4	2.6
$f(x)$	3.120 14	4.425 69	6.042 41	8.030 14	10.466 75

With this information only, state the values of n for which it is possible to calculate the approximation M_n to $\int_{1.8}^{2.6} f(x)\, dx$.
Calculate M_n for each of these values of n.

The trapezium rule

The principle of the trapezium rule is similar to that of the mid-point rule. A series of regular shapes with areas that are easily calculated is used to approximate a given area. In this case each shape is a trapezium rather than a rectangle.

In figure 3.7 four trapezia, each with the same width, h, are used to approximate the area under the curve $y = f(x)$ between $x = a$ and $x = b$.

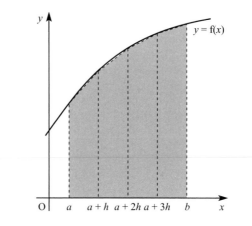

Figure 3.7

The left-most trapezium has its base running from a to $a + h$. The lengths of its parallel sides are $f(a)$ and $f(a + h)$ and so the area of this trapezium is

$$\frac{h}{2}(f(a) + f(a + h)).$$

Similarly, the lengths of the parallel sides of the next trapezium are $f(a + h)$ and $f(a + 2h)$ and so the area of the second trapezium is

$$\frac{h}{2}(f(a + h) + f(a + 2h)).$$

Proceeding in this way, the total area of the four trapezia is

$$\frac{h}{2}[f(a) + f(a+h)] + \frac{h}{2}[f(a+h) + f(a+2h)] + \frac{h}{2}[f(a+2h) + f(a+3h)] + \frac{h}{2}[f(a+3h) + f(b)]$$

$$= \frac{h}{2}(f(a) + f(a+h) + f(a+h) + f(a+2h) + f(a+2h) + f(a+3h) + f(a+3h) + f(b))$$

$$= \frac{h}{2}(f(a) + 2[f(a+h) + f(a+2h) + f(a+3h)] + f(b))$$

This particular approximation to $\int_a^b f(x)\mathrm{d}x$ is called T_4. This means the trapezium rule approximation with four strips.

Obviously you can use any number of strips you like. Again you would expect that, in general, the more strips you use the more accurate the approximation to the area will be.

The general form of the trapezium rule using n strips (resulting in n trapezia), each of width h, is usually expressed using the following notation.

- $f_0 = f(a)$, the value of the function at the left-hand end of the first strip.

- $f_1 = f(a + h)$, the value of the function at the left-hand end of the second strip (or the right-hand end of the first strip) and so on.

- Finally, $f_n = f(a + nh) = f(b)$, the value of the function at the right-hand end of the nth strip.

Summing the areas of the n trapezia gives the following approximation to $\int_a^b f(x)\mathrm{d}x$.

$$T_n = \frac{h}{2}(f_0 + f_1) + \frac{h}{2}(f_1 + f_2) + \dots + \frac{h}{2}(f_{n-2} + f_{n-1}) + \frac{h}{2}(f_{n-1} + f_n)$$

$$= \frac{h}{2}[f_0 + 2(f_1 + f_2 + f_3 + \dots + f_{n-1}) + f_n]$$

Below, as an example, the trapezium rule approximations, T_1, T_2, T_4 and T_8, to the area beneath the graph of $f(x) = \cos x$ between $a = 0$ radians and $b = \frac{\pi}{2}$ radians are calculated.

The value T_1 is calculated by approximating the area using a single trapezium (see figure 3.8). Its base stretches from $a = 0$ to $a + h = \frac{\pi}{2}$.

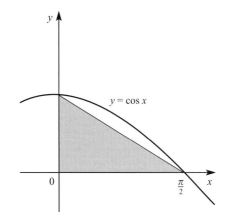

Figure 3.8

The parallel sides of the trapezium have lengths of $f(0) = 1$ and $f\left(\frac{\pi}{2}\right) = 0$ respectively. (This means that the 'trapezium' is in fact a triangle as you can see in figure 3.8.) Its area is then

$$T_1 = \frac{h}{2}\left(f(0) + f\left(\frac{\pi}{2}\right)\right)$$

$$= \frac{\frac{\pi}{2}}{2}(1 + 0)$$

$$= \frac{\pi}{4} = 0.785\,398\,163 \text{ (to 9 d.p.).}$$

For T_2, divide the interval into two strips both with width $h = \frac{\pi}{4}$. The first of of these goes from $a = 0$ to $a + h = \frac{\pi}{4}$ and the second from $a + h = \frac{\pi}{4}$ to $b = a + 2h = \frac{\pi}{2}$ (see figure 3.9).

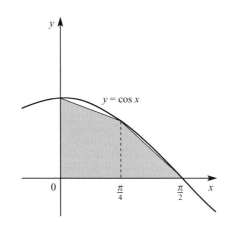

Figure 3.9

The total area is given by

$$T_2 = \frac{h}{2} \times (f(a) + 2f(a + h) + f(a + 2h))$$

$$= \frac{\frac{\pi}{4}}{2}\left(\cos(0) + 2\cos\left(\frac{\pi}{4}\right) + \cos\left(\frac{\pi}{2}\right)\right).$$

$$= 0.948\,059\,449 \text{ (to 9 d.p.).}$$

Similarly, with $h = \frac{\pi}{8}$,

$$T_4 = \frac{h}{2} \times (f(a) + 2[f(a + h) + f(a + 2h) + f(a + 3h)] + f(a + 4h))$$

$$= \frac{\frac{\pi}{8}}{2}\left(\cos(0) + 2 \times \left[\cos\left(\frac{\pi}{8}\right) + \cos\left(\frac{2\pi}{8}\right) + \cos\left(\frac{3\pi}{8}\right)\right] + \cos\left(\frac{4\pi}{8}\right)\right)$$

$$= 0.987\,115\,801 \text{ (to 9 d.p.).}$$

And with $h = \frac{\pi}{16}$,

$$T_8 = \frac{h}{2} \times (f(a) + 2[f(a + h) + f(a + 2h) + \dots + f(a + 7h)] + f(a + 8h))$$

$$= \frac{\frac{\pi}{16}}{2}\left(\cos(0) + 2 \times \left[\cos\left(\frac{\pi}{16}\right) + \cos\left(\frac{2\pi}{16}\right) + \dots + \cos\left(\frac{7\pi}{16}\right)\right] + \cos\left(\frac{8\pi}{16}\right)\right)$$

$$= 0.996\,785\,172 \text{ (to 9 d.p.).}$$

? Look at figures 3.8 and 3.9.
In this case is the trapezium rule underestimating or overestimating the area?

EXAMPLE 3.2

Use the following data to estimate $\int_1^5 f(x)\,dx$ using the trapezium rule.

x	1.0	1.5	2.0	2.5	3.0	3.5	4.0	4.5	5.0
$f(x)$	0.00	0.41	0.69	0.92	1.10	1.25	1.39	1.50	1.61

SOLUTION

It is good practice to set down the calculation in a form which can be easily checked. One possible layout is shown in the following table.

x	f(x)	Factor	Product
1.0	0.00	1	0.00
1.5	0.41	2	0.82
2.0	0.69	2	1.38
2.5	0.92	2	1.84
3.0	1.10	2	2.20
3.5	1.25	2	2.50
4.0	1.39	2	2.78
4.5	1.50	2	3.00
5.0	1.61	1	1.61

The total of the product column is 16.13.

$h = 0.5$ and so

$$\int_1^5 f(x)\,dx \approx \frac{0.5}{2} \times 16.13 = 4.03.$$

ACTIVITY 3.2

1 In figure 3.10, the two points, A and B, on the x axis, are 2 units apart. All the strips are of equal width. The values of f_i for $i = 0, 1, 2, 3, 4$ are given in the table.

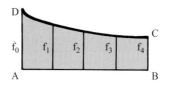

Figure 3.10

i	0	1	2	3	4
f_i	1.0	0.67	0.5	0.4	0.3

Estimate the shaded area, using the trapezium rule.

2 Estimate $\int_0^1 \frac{1}{1 + x^3}\,dx$ using the trapezium rule with

(i) $h = 1$

(ii) $h = 0.5$

(iii) $h = 0.25$.

1 Use the trapezium rule with five strips to approximate the following integrals. Carry as many decimal places as you can in your working.

(i) $\int_0^{0.5} \sqrt{1 + x^3}\,dx$

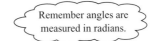
Remember angles are measured in radians.

(ii) $\int_0^1 \cos(1 + x^2)\,dx$

2 (i) Using a calculator or spreadsheet program, find the approximations T_1, T_2 and T_4 to the following integrals to 4 decimal places. Carry as many decimal places as you can in your working.

(a) $\int_0^1 x^2\,dx$

(b) $\int_0^{0.5} \sin(x^2)\,dx$

(c) $\int_0^2 (\sin x + \cos x)\,dx$

(ii) Calculate the exact value of the integral in part (i) (a) and then calculate and comment upon the error in each of the approximations you found.

3 A function f has the values given in the following table.

x	1.8	2.0	2.2	2.4	2.6
$f(x)$	3.120 14	4.425 69	6.042 41	8.030 14	10.466 75

With this information only, state the values of n for which it is possible to calculate the approximation T_n to $\int_{1.8}^{2.6} f(x)\,dx$.

Calculate T_n for each of these values of n.

4 The values of the function $f(x)$ are known correct to 4 decimal places as shown in the following table.

x	0	0.1	0.2	0.3	0.4	0.5	0.6	0.7	0.8
$f(x)$	0.7348	0.6924	0.6417	0.5823	0.5144	0.4382	0.3545	0.2643	0.1691

Estimate $I = \int_0^{0.8} f(x)\,dx$ using the trapezium rule with $h = 0.8$, $h = 0.4$, $h = 0.2$ and $h = 0.1$.

Using the mid-point rule and the trapezium rule together

There is a connection between the trapezium rule and the mid-point rule which can be used to shorten calculations. This is that for any fixed value of n, T_{2n} is the average of T_n and M_n. In other words,

$$T_{2n} = \frac{T_n + M_n}{2}$$

For example

$$T_2 = \frac{T_1 + M_1}{2}.$$

So, if you have calculated the T_1 and M_1 approximations to an area, you can calculate T_2 quickly by taking the average of T_1 and M_1.

Similarly $T_4 = \dfrac{T_2 + M_2}{2}$, T_4 is the average of T_2 and M_2.

$T_8 = \dfrac{T_4 + M_4}{2}$ and so on. T_8 is the average of T_4 and M_4.

EXAMPLE 3.3

Calculate the trapezium rule approximations T_1, T_2 and T_4 and the mid-point rule approximations M_1 and M_2 to the integral $\int_{0.5}^{1.5} \sin x^2 \, dx$ as efficiently as possible.

SOLUTION

The values of the function $f(x) = \sin x^2$ that are required are given in the table.

The interval has to be divided into four strips for the approximations required.

x	0.5	0.75	1	1.25	1.5
$f(x)$	0.247 403 959	0.533 302 673	0.841 470 984	0.999 965 585	0.778 073 196

$M_1 = 1 \times f(1) = 0.841 470 984$

$T_1 = \frac{1}{2}(f(0.5) + f(1.5)) = 0.512 738 578$ Calculate, M_1, T_1 and M_2 as usual.

$M_2 = \frac{1}{2} \times (f(0.75) + f(1.25)) = 0.766 634 129$

Then

$$T_2 = \frac{T_1 + M_1}{2} = 0.677 104 781$$

and

$$T_4 = \frac{T_2 + M_2}{2} = 0.721 869 456$$

Using the fact that for any fixed value of n, $T_{2n} = \dfrac{T_n + M_n}{2}$.

? For the general integral $\int_a^b f(x) dx$ with $h = \dfrac{b-a}{2}$,

(i) explain why

$$M_1 = 2h \times f(a+h),\ T_1 = h \times [f(a) + f(b)] \text{ and } T_2 = \frac{h}{2}[f(a) + 2f(a+h) + f(b)]$$

(ii) show that $T_2 = \dfrac{T_1 + M_1}{2}$

(iii) generalise this to show that $T_{2n} = \dfrac{T_n + M_n}{2}$ for any value of n.

Producing upper and lower bounds for an integral

The curves in figure 3.11 are both the graph of a function f(x). The area beneath the curve $y = f(x)$ between $x = a$ and $x = b$ and the x axis is concave in this example.

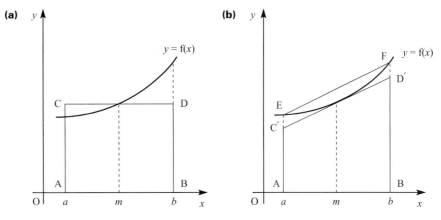

Figure 3.11

The mid-point rule estimate, M_1, to $\int_a^b f(x)dx$ is the area of the rectangle ACDB in figure 3.11(a).

The trapezium rule estimate, T_1 to $\int_a^b f(x)dx$ is the area of the trapezium AEFB in figure 3.11(b).

In figure 3.11(b), the lines C′D′ and EF are parallel. The area of the rectangle ACDB in figure 3.11(a) is in fact the same as the area of the trapezium AC′D′B in figure 3.11(b).

 Why is the area of the rectangle ACDB in figure 3.11(a) the same as the area of the trapezium AC′D′B in figure 3.11(b)?

Using this observation, it can be seen that

$$M_1 < \int_a^b f(x)dx < T_1.$$

 Why?

So M_1 is an underestimate of $\int_a^b f(x)dx$ and T_1 is an overestimate of $\int_a^b f(x)dx$.

❓ Figure 3.12 shows the graph of a function f(x) between values $x = a$ and $x = b$. This time, the area beneath $y = $ f(x) between $x = a$, $x = b$ and the x axis is convex.

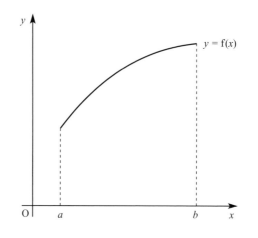

Figure 3.12

Draw diagrams similar to those in figure 3.11, to show that, for this function,

$$T_1 < \int_a^b f(x)\,dx < M_1.$$

In fact, for most well-behaved functions, for areas under convex or concave sections of their graph you will find that this is the case. You will also find that, for such areas, T_n will be an underestimate to the area when M_n is an overestimate to the area and vice versa.

This observation is important for two reasons.

- It means that it is possible to produce upper and lower bounds for the exact area (in other words, to give an interval estimate for it) and hence give the area to a specified degree of accuracy.

- It leads to the development of another method for approximating area. This is called Simpson's rule.

Simpson's rule

The mid-point rule estimates M_1, M_2, M_4 and M_8 and the trapezium rule estimates, T_1, T_2, T_4 and T_8 to $\int_0^{\frac{\pi}{2}} \cos x \, dx$, calculated earlier in this chapter are displayed in the table, along with T_{16}, T_{32}, M_{16} and M_{32}. All the values have been rounded to 9 decimal places.

n	T_n	M_n
1	0.785 398 163	1.110 720 735
2	0.948 059 449	1.026 172 153
4	0.987 115 801	1.006 454 543
8	0.996 785 172	1.001 608 189
16	0.999 196 680	1.000 401 708
32	0.999 799 194	1.000 100 406

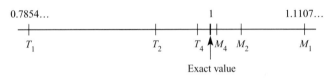

$0.9997 \ldots < \int_0^{\frac{\pi}{2}} \cos x \, dx < 1.0001 \ldots$

This means that the integral is 1.000 correct to 3 decimal places.

In fact, in your pure mathematics course, in C3 Chapter 5 you learn how to calculate that the value of this integral is exactly 1.

These values (for $n = 1, 2$ and 4) are represented on the number line in figure 3.13.

0.7854... 1 1.1107...

T_1 T_2 T_4 M_4 M_2 M_1

Exact value

Figure 3.13

Notice that T_1 is an underestimate and M_1 is an overestimate. The same is true of T_2 and M_2, T_4 and M_4 and so on.

Moreover

- the absolute error in T_1 is 0.2146, which is about twice as much as 0.1107, the absolute error in M_1

- the absolute error in T_2 is 0.0519 which is about twice as much as 0.026, the error in M_2

- similar comments apply both to T_4 and M_4 and so on.

 Check that the same is true for T_8 and M_8, T_{16} and M_{16} and T_{32} and M_{32}.

The value

$$\frac{2M_n + T_n}{3}$$

is a weighted average of M_n and T_n. The usual average is exactly in the middle of M_n and T_n on the number line. This weighted average is twice as close to M_n as it is to T_n. This is justified by the differences in the errors associated with these values, as discussed above.

This is *Simpson's rule* and the value above is called S_n.

$$S_n = \frac{2M_n + T_n}{3}$$

 Explain why S_n is the average of the three values M_n, M_n and T_n.

So you can calculate the approximations S_1, S_2, S_4, S_8, S_{16} and S_{32} to $\int_0^{\frac{\pi}{2}} \cos x \, dx$ from the values of M_1, M_2, M_4, M_8, M_{16} and M_{32} and of T_1, T_2, T_4, T_8, T_{16} and T_{32} given again below. As before, all the values have been rounded to 9 decimal places.

n	T_n	M_n	$S_n = \dfrac{2M_n + T_n}{3}$
1	0.785 398 163	1.110 720 735	1.002 279 877
2	0.948 059 449	1.026 172 153	1.000 134 585
4	0.987 115 801	1.006 454 543	1.000 008 296
8	0.996 785 172	1.001 608 189	1.000 000 517
16	0.999 196 680	1.000 401 708	1.000 000 032
32	0.999 799 194	1.000 100 406	1.000 000 002

Historical note

Thomas Simpson (1710–61) was a weaver from Spitalfields who taught himself mathematics and, as a break from working at his loom, taught mathematics to others. A textbook which he wrote in 1745 ran to eight editions, the last of which was published in 1809. He became Professor of Mathematics at Woolwich College and was noted for his work on trigonometrical proofs and for the derivation of formulae for use in the computation of tables of values of trigonometrical functions. The result with which his name is associated had been published in draft form by the Scottish mathematician James Gregory in 1668 and was published in complete form by Simpson in his 'Mathematical Dissertation on Physical and Analytical Subjects' in 1743.

EXAMPLE 3.4

For the integral $\int_1^2 \sqrt{1 + \cos x} \, dx$

(i) find the values of T_1 and M_1 and hence obtain the value of S_1, giving your answers to 6 decimal places

(ii) find similarly the values of T_2, M_2, S_2, T_4, M_4 and S_4.

SOLUTION

Let $f(x) = \sqrt{1 + \cos x}$.

(i) $M_1 = 1 \times f(1.5)$

$\qquad = 1.034\,764$ (to 6 d.p.)

> Remember x is radians.

$T_1 = \frac{1}{2}(f(1) + f(2))$

$\qquad = 1.002\,596$ (to 6 d.p.)

$S_1 = \dfrac{2M_1 + T_1}{3}$

> Using $S_n = \dfrac{2M_n + T_n}{3}$.

$\qquad = 1.024\,042$ (to 6 d.p.)

(ii) $T_2 = \dfrac{M_1 + T_1}{2}$

> Using $T_{2n} = \dfrac{T_n + M_n}{2}$.

$\qquad = 1.018\,680$ (to 6 d.p.)

$M_2 = \frac{1}{2}(f(1.25) + f(1.75))$

$\qquad = 1.026\,691$ (to 6 d.p.)

$S_2 = \dfrac{2M_2 + T_2}{3}$

$\qquad = 1.024\,021$ (to 6 d.p.)

$T_4 = \dfrac{M_2 + T_2}{2}$

$\qquad = 1.022\,685$ (to 6 d.p.)

$M_4 = \frac{1}{4}(f(1.125) + f(1.375) + f(1.625) + f(1.875))$

$\qquad = 1.024\,686$ (to 6 d.p.)

$S_4 = \dfrac{2M_4 + T_4}{3}$

$\qquad = 1.024\,019$ (to 6 d.p.)

The Simpson's rule approximation S_n to the integral $\int_a^b f(x)\,dx$ can be calculated directly from function values.

Divide the interval from a to b into $2n$ strips, each of width h. As usual let f_0 be the value of the function at a, f_1 the value at the right-hand end of the first strip and so on so that f_{2n} is the value of the function at b. Then

$$S_n = \frac{h}{3}[f_0 + f_{2n} + 4(f_1 + f_3 + f_5 + \ldots + f_{2n-1}) + 2(f_2 + f_4 + f_6 + \ldots + f_{2n-2})].$$

You may have made some observations about the error in each of the methods and their rate of convergence to the exact value of the integral. These will be discussed further in Chapter 6.

1 The diagram shows a graph of $y = \sqrt{x^3 + 1}$.

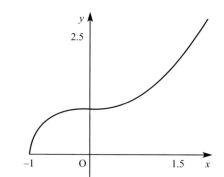

Use the mid-point rule and the trapezium rule to give the value of
$I = \int_0^1 \sqrt{x^3 + 1}\ \mathrm{d}x$ correct to 2 decimal places.
(Hint: One rule will give an overestimate of I and the other an underestimate).

2 The diagram shows a graph of $y = x^x$.

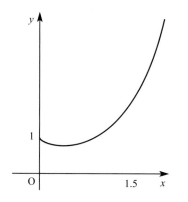

Use the mid-point rule and the trapezium rule to give the value of $I = \int_{0.5}^{1.5} x^x\,\mathrm{d}x$ correct to 1 decimal place.
(Hint: Produce an interval estimate for I.)

3 Find, to 6 decimal places, the approximations S_1, S_2 and S_4 of the integral $\int_0^2 \sqrt{1 + \sin x + \cos x}\ \mathrm{d}x$.

4 The values of a function $f(x)$ are known only for the values of x shown in the following table.

x	0	0.1	0.2	0.4
$f(x)$	1.270	1.662	2.138	4.535

(i) With this information, what is the largest value of n for which it is possible to calculate S_n as an approximation to $\int_0^{0.4} f(x)\mathrm{d}x$.

(ii) If the value of $f(0.3)$ now becomes available, what is the largest such value of n?

5 Prove that, for any value of n, $S_n = \dfrac{4T_{2n} - T_n}{3}$.

☆

6 A function $f(x)$ has values correct to 3 decimal places as shown in the table.

x	0	2	4
$f(x)$	7.389	11.023	16.445

The value of $\int_0^4 f(x)\,dx$ is denoted by I.

(i) Obtain estimates of I using
  (a) the trapezium rule and the ordinates $f(0)$ and $f(4)$ only
  (b) the mid-point rule
  (c) Simpson's rule.

(ii) You are now given further values of the function, also correct to 3 decimal places, as shown.

x	0.5	1	1.5	2.5	3	3.5
$f(x)$	8.166	9.025	9.974	12.182	13.464	14.880

Find two further Simpson's rule estimates of I.

[MEI, *part*]

7 An estimate of the value of the following integral is required.

$$\int_0^2 \sqrt{1 + x^2}\,dx$$

(i) Calculate the values of T_1, M_1 and S_1.
  Copy the table below and record these values, correct to 6 decimal places.

$T_1 =$	$S_1 =$
$M_1 =$	
$T_2 =$	$S_2 =$
$M_2 =$	
$T_4 =$	$S_4 =$
$M_4 =$	

(ii) Obtain, as efficiently as possible, the other values required to complete the table.

(iii) Use the values in the table
  (a) to give the value of the integral to a level of accuracy you feel is justified
  (b) to show that the magnitudes of the errors in the mid-point rule are about half of those in the corresponding trapezium rule.

1 The value of an integral can be approximated by the mid-point rule using the formula

$$\int_a^b f(x)\, dx \approx M_n = h(f(m_1) + f(m_2) + \dots + f(m_n))$$

where $m_1, m_2, \dots, m_n$ are the values of x at the mid-points of n strips, each of width h.

2 The value of an integral can be approximated by the trapezium rule using n strips, each of width h, using the formula

$$\int_a^b f(x)\, dx \approx T_n = \frac{h}{2}[f_0 + 2(f_1 + f_2 + f_3 + \dots + f_{n-1}) + f_n]$$

where, $f_0 = f(a)$ is the value of the function at the left-hand end of the first strip, $f_1 = f(a + h)$ is the value of the function at the left-hand end of the second strip (or the right-hand end of the first strip) and so on. Finally, $f_n = f(a + nh) = f(b)$ is the value of the function at the right-hand end of the nth strip.

3 $T_{2n} = \dfrac{T_n + M_n}{2}$ for any value of n.

4 For most well-behaved functions, for areas under concave or convex sections of their graph, T_n will be an underestimate of $\int_a^b f(x)\, dx$ when M_n is an overestimate of $\int_a^b f(x)\, dx$ and vice versa.

5 The value of an integral can be approximated by Simpson's rule using the formula

$$S_n = \frac{2M_n + T_n}{3}.$$

Approximating functions

It is the mark of an educated mind to rest satisfied with the degree of precision which the nature of the subject admits and not to seek exactness where only an approximation is possible.

Aristotle

A common thread running through the work of many people, for example engineers, economists, biologists and managers, is the need to know the nature of relationships between different quantities.

Leading financiers would be pleased to know how the Bank of England interest rates and the volume of goods the UK exports are linked. If it were possible to derive a reliable formula to describe this relationship it would be worth its weight in gold! This problem is made more complicated by the fact that numerous other variables influence how much the UK exports.

In this chapter, the simpler, though far from trivial, problem of the relationship between two quantities dependent only on each other is considered. First look at an example which can be solved easily.

A British holiday maker in Europe finds that the number of euros given in exchange for pounds sterling at a certain bank, were as shown in the following table.

Pounds, p	10	20	30	40
Euros, e	13.10	28.20	43.30	58.40

A formula is needed which gives the number of euros, e, obtained in exchange for p pounds.

Figure 4.1 shows the graph of e plotted against p. Since the points lie on a straight line, it is a simple matter to obtain a formula linking e and p.

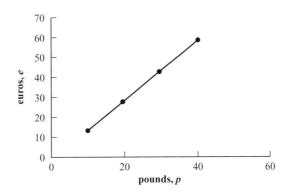

Figure 4.1

❓ The required relationship is $e = 1.51p - 2$.
How could you find this relationship?

The problem is more challenging when the points do not lie on a straight line. For example, consider the following.

As a young person develops, his or her growth rate, measured in centimetres per year, is not constant. Measurements were made of the average increase in height per year of a group of young people at different ages and the results are shown below.

Age (years)	2	6	10	14	18
Growth rate (cm per year)	7.8	6.0	4.8	7.0	1.1

Figure 4.2 shows a graph of the data plotted with age on the x axis and growth rate on the y axis.

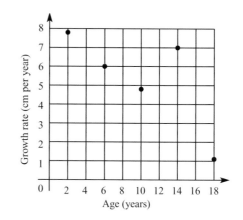

Figure 4.2

Is it possible to find a formula which gives the growth rate for the ages 2, 6, 10, 14 and 18?

Perhaps surprisingly, the answer to this question is yes!

In fact the following function gives the growth rate, y, in terms of the years, x, for $x = 2, 6, 10, 14$ and 18. (The coefficients have been rounded to 8 decimal places.)

$$f(x) = 4.139\,843\,75 + 3.347\,916\,67x - 0.913\,151\,04x^2 + 0.081\,770\,83x^3 - 0.002\,327\,47x^4$$

Figure 4.3 shows the graph of this function and the data points. The function provides a good model for the growth rate between 0 and 18 years.

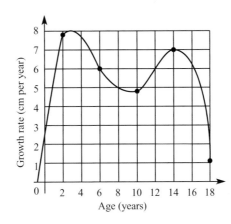

Figure 4.3

In this chapter you will learn how this function has been calculated. The method enables you to calculate a polynomial which passes through any given set of points with evenly spaced x co-ordinates.

Notation

Look at the following table. It gives the values of a function f for some evenly spaced x values.

x	4	7	10	13
$f(x)$	4.8	7.1	6.9	10.4

The standard notation throughout this chapter for this will be as follows.

x	x_0	x_1	x_2	x_3
$f(x)$	f_0	f_1	f_2	f_3

Obviously this notation can deal with any number of x values and their corresponding function values.

- x_0 is the leftmost of all the x values and f_0 is the value of the function there.

- x_1 is the x value to the right of x_0, with f_1 the value of the function at x_1, and so on.

In addition, the x values of 2, 4, 6 and 8 can be described as

$$x = 2 \, (2) \, 8.$$

This means that the x values begin at 2 and end at 8, with steps of 2.

For example, $x = 1 \, (0.25) \, 2$ means the x values are 1, 1.25, 1.5, 1.75 and 2.

Throughout this chapter the letter h is used to denote the constant spacing between the x values.

Finite difference tables

The method for finding a polynomial with a graph that passes through the given points begins with the creation of a *finite difference table*. This table includes

- the *x* values, these should be evenly spaced
- the function values at these values
- the differences between consecutive function values
- the differences between these differences and so on.

The symbol Δ (the capital of the Greek letter delta, δ) denotes the *forward difference operator*. It means 'take the difference between two consecutive values'. It is used as follows.

$$\Delta f_0 = f_1 - f_0, \quad \Delta f_1 = f_2 - f_1$$

You can look at the differences between these differences. This is denoted by Δ^2. For example

$$\Delta^2 f_0 = \Delta f_1 - \Delta f_0, \quad \Delta^2 f_1 = \Delta f_2 - \Delta f_1.$$

A table can be created which includes all these values for a given set of data points.

The table below shows how this is done for a small set of data points.

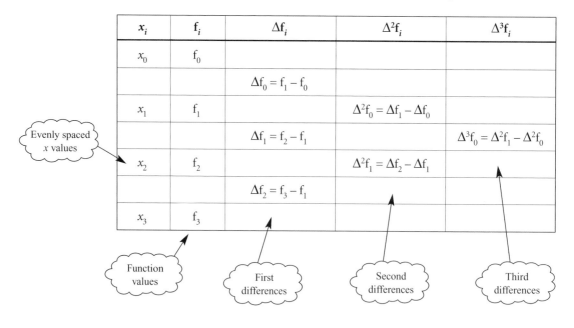

How would such a table change for a larger set of data points?

EXAMPLE 4.1   Construct the finite difference table for the set of data points given below.

x_i	2	4	6	8
f_i	7.8	6.0	6.0	6.5

SOLUTION

x_i	f_i	Δf_i	$\Delta^2 f_i$	$\Delta^3 f_i$
2	7.8			
		$6 - 7.8 = -1.8$		
4	6		$0 - (-1.8) = 1.8$	
		$6 - 6 = 0$		$0.5 - 1.8 = -1.3$
6	6		$0.5 - 0 = 0.5$	
		$6.5 - 6 = 0.5$		
8	6.5			

You should set out your difference table like this. Usually you would not include the working in such a table; this is only shown here for clarity.

Of course, the size of the finite difference table obtained depends upon the number of data points you have been given. The next example shows this.

EXAMPLE 4.2   The following table gives values of a function $f(x)$ for equally spaced value of x. Construct a finite difference table for these data.

x_i	−2	−1	0	1	2
f_i	−27	−4	1	0	5

SOLUTION

x_i	f_i	Δf_i	$\Delta^2 f_i$	$\Delta^3 f_i$	$\Delta^4 f_i$
−2	−27				
		23			
−1	−4		−18		
		5		12	
0	1		−6		0
		−1		12	
1	0		6		
		5			
2	5				

⚠ The two most common mistakes that are made with difference tables are as follows.

- Subtracting numbers in the wrong order.
  Remember, for example, that $\Delta f_0 = f_1 - f_0$ and *not* $f_0 - f_1$. (So if a number in a difference table is smaller than the one below it, the corresponding difference in the next column is positive.)

- Thinking that $\Delta^2 f_0 = (\Delta f_0)^2$. *It does not.*
  This confusion is caused by a weakness of the notation; try not be a victim of this kind of mistake.

Before looking at the polynomial to fit given data points, it is useful to look at difference tables for points on the graph of some polynomial functions. This will show you how to predict the degree of polynomial needed to fit a given set of data points.

First look at the behaviour of the differences in the values of the linear function, $y = 3x + 5$, for some equally spaced x values.

x	$y = 3x + 5$	Δy	$\Delta^2 y$	$\Delta^3 y$
0	5			
		3		
1	8		0	
		3		0
2	11		0	
		3		
3	14			

❓ For a difference table, explain why, if the nth differences are constant, then the $(n + 1)$th differences are zero and vice versa.

Next, look at the differences in the values of the quadratic function, $y = x^2 + 3x + 5$, for some equally spaced x values.

x	$y = x^2 + 3x + 5$	Δy	$\Delta^2 y$	$\Delta^3 y$	$\Delta^4 y$
0	5				
		4			
1	9		2		
		6		0	
2	15		2		0
		8		0	
3	23		2		
		10			
4	33				

ACTIVITY 4.1

Repeat the above beginning with a cubic and then a quartic of your choice. (You may wish to use more x values.)

What do you notice?

You should have seen that for a cubic the third differences are constant, for a quartic the fourth differences are constant. In general, for a polynomial with degree n, the nth differences will be constant.

The exciting fact, and the key to calculating polynomials that fit the given points exactly, is that the converse of this is also true. The process works in reverse.

For example, if you have a set of data points for which the third differences are constant then a cubic (or possibly a polynomial of lesser degree) will fit the data. If the fourth differences are constant then a quartic (or a polynomial of lesser degree) will fit the data.

This polynomial is called the *Newton interpolating polynomial.* You will find out how to calculate it in the next section.

EXERCISE 4A

1 The following table gives the values of a function $f(x)$ for equally spaced values of x.

Construct a finite difference table for these data.

x_i	3	5	7	9	11
f_i	21	11	14	8	10

2 The following table gives the values of a function $f(x)$ for equally spaced values of x.

Construct a finite difference table for these data.

x_i	−3	0	3	6	9
f_i	0	4	11	21	34

3 List the values of x described by the following.

   (i) $x = -0.25\ (0.25)\ 1.5$ **(ii)** $x = 1.0\ (0.1)\ 2.0$

   (iii) $x = 0\ (0.01)\ 0.1$ **(iv)** $x = 1.0\ (0.125)\ 2.0$

   (v) $x = -2\ (1)\ 2$

4 Given that $f(x) = x^3 - 3x^2$, construct a finite difference table for the function f for $x = 0.0\ (0.2)\ 1.0$.

5 Construct a finite difference table for the function $f(x) = x^4$ for $x = 0.0\ (0.1)\ 0.5$

   (i) when the values of $f(x)$ are exact

   (ii) when the values of $f(x)$ are rounded to 3 decimal places.

   Comment on the higher-order differences in the two tables.

6 Construct a finite difference table for the values of $\sin x$ rounded to 3 decimal places, for $x = 0.0\ (0.2)\ 1.0$.

   Write down the maximum possible error in the numbers in each column in your table caused by rounding the function values to 3 decimal places.

7 Prove the following are true.

   ☆ **(i)** $\Delta^2 f_0 = f_2 - 2f_1 + f_0$

   ☆ **(ii)** $\Delta^3 f_0 = f_3 - 3f_2 + 3f_1 - f_0$

   ☆ (Hint: It may be useful to think about where each of the numbers occurs in a finite difference table.)

The Newton interpolating polynomial

The idea of estimating the value of a function between known values has been used throughout history. This technique is known as *interpolation*. Predicting the positions of the planets, ocean navigation, the study of population growth and life insurance are just a few examples of situations in which interpolation has been used.

The Newton interpolating polynomial (sometimes called Newton's forward difference formula) is given by

$$f(x) = f_0 + \frac{x - x_0}{h}\Delta f_0 + \frac{(x - x_0)(x - x_1)}{2!h^2}\Delta^2 f_0 + \frac{(x - x_0)(x - x_1)(x - x_2)}{3!h^3}\Delta^3 f_0 + \ldots .$$

It is expressed in terms of the notation already introduced (remember, h is the spacing between the x values). It has the property that its graph passes exactly through the given set of data points from which it is calculated.

● Initially it looks quite complicated but it is actually very easy to remember, just remember the pattern for consecutive terms.

● The formula is not an infinite sum. It should be terminated after the number of terms determined by your particular requirements and/or the number of data points you are dealing with.

To convince yourself that it does do what it claims to and to familiarise yourself with its use, start by applying it to a situation where the function is known.

EXAMPLE 4.3

The cubic $f(x) = x^3 - 2x + 1$ passes through the points $(-1, 2)$, $(0, 1)$, $(1, 0)$ and $(2, 5)$. Show that Newton's interpolating polynomial for these four points is the original cubic polynomial.

SOLUTION

Recall the formula for the Newton interpolating polynomial.

$$f(x) = f_0 + \frac{x - x_0}{h}\Delta f_0 + \frac{(x - x_0)(x - x_1)}{2!h^2}\Delta^2 f_0 + \frac{(x - x_0)(x - x_1)(x - x_2)}{3!h^3}\Delta^3 f_0 + \dots$$

The finite difference table for this data is given below.

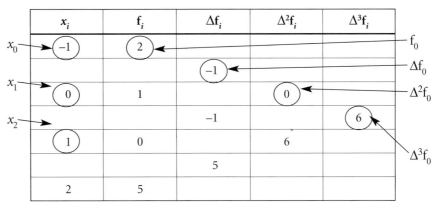

The four points, $(-1, 2)$, $(0, 1)$, $(1, 0)$ and $(2, 5)$ give the x_i and the f_i values.

So, substituting in the formula and with $h = 1$, gives

$$f(x) = f_0 + \frac{x - x_0}{h}\Delta f_0 + \frac{(x - x_0)(x - x_1)}{2!h^2}\Delta^2 f_0 + \frac{(x - x_0)(x - x_1)(x - x_2)}{3!h^3}\Delta^3 f_0$$

$$= 2 + [(x-(-1))\times(-1)] + \left[\frac{(x-(-1))(x-0)}{2}\times 0\right] + \left[\frac{(x-(-1))(x-0)(x-1)}{6}\times 6\right]$$

$$= 2 + (-x - 1) + 0 + (x + 1)x(x - 1)$$

$$= 2 - x - 1 + x^3 - x$$

$$= x^3 - 2x + 1$$

Notice how the formula has been terminated at the term involving $\Delta^3 f_0$ because with four data points you can calculate only as far as third differences, a cubic or polynomial of lesser degree will always fit the data.

as required.

? How many points on a straight line do you need to be told in order to calculate the equation of that straight line?

How many points on a quadratic do you need to know in order to calculate its equation?

How many points for a cubic?

What degree of polynomial do you think will fit a set of n data points with evenly spaces x values?

You have seen that the formula for the Newton interpolating polynomial seems to work. Now think about why this is the case.

The Newton interpolating polynomial is

$$f(x) = f_0 + \frac{x - x_0}{h}\Delta f_0 + \frac{(x - x_0)(x - x_1)}{2!h^2}\Delta^2 f_0 + \frac{(x - x_0)(x - x_1)(x - x_2)}{3!h^3}\Delta^3 f_0 + \dots$$

Substituting $x = x_0$ into this formula gives

$$f(x_0) = f_0 + \frac{x_0 - x_0}{h}\Delta f_0 + \frac{(x_0 - x_0)(x_0 - x_1)}{2!h^2}\Delta^2 f_0 + \frac{(x_0 - x_0)(x_0 - x_1)(x_0 - x_2)}{3!h^3}\Delta^3 f_0 + \dots$$

$$= f_0.$$

> All these terms are zero as they each contain $(x_0 - x_0)$ as a factor.

Substituting $x = x_1$ into this formula gives

$$f(x_1) = f_0 + \frac{x_1 - x_0}{h}\Delta f_0 + \frac{(x_1 - x_0)(x_1 - x_1)}{2!h^2}\Delta^2 f_0 + \frac{(x_1 - x_0)(x_1 - x_1)(x_1 - x_2)}{3!h^3}\Delta^3 f_0 + \dots$$

$$= f_0 + \frac{h}{h}\Delta f_0$$

$$= f_0 + \Delta f_0$$

$$= f_1.$$

> Since $(x_1 - x_0) = h$, and again every other term is zero.

Substituting $x = x_2$ into this formula gives

$$f(x_2) = f_0 + \frac{x_2 - x_0}{h}\Delta f_0 + \frac{(x_2 - x_0)(x_2 - x_1)}{2!h^2}\Delta^2 f_0 + \frac{(x_2 - x_0)(x_2 - x_1)(x_2 - x_2)}{3!h^3}\Delta^3 f_0 + \dots$$

$$= f_0 + \frac{2h}{h}\Delta f_0 + \frac{2h \times h}{2h^2}\Delta^2 f_0$$

$$= f_0 + 2\Delta f_0 + \Delta^2 f_0$$

$$= (f_0 + \Delta f_0) + (\Delta f_0 + \Delta^2 f_0)$$

$$= f_1 + \Delta f_1$$

$$= f_2.$$

> Since $(x_2 - x_0) = 2h$, $(x_2 - x_1) = h$ and every other term is zero.

And so on....

 Substitute $x = x_3$ into the formula and show that $f(x_3) = f_3$.

Using the interpolating polynomial to approximate the value of a function

The interpolating polynomial can be used to get an approximation of the value of a function at an x value *between* those where its value is known. The idea is simply to evaluate the Newton interpolating polynomial at that x value. If this is all you require, you can save yourself some work by substituting the x value into the formula for the interpolating polynomial instead of calculating the polynomial itself first.

This is shown in the next example.

EXAMPLE 4.4

The following table gives the values of a function $f(x)$ for equally spaced values of x. Construct a table of finite differences as far as fourth differences and use the Newton interpolation formula to estimate $f(1.21)$.

x_i	-2	-1	0	1	2
f_i	-27	-4	1	0	5

SOLUTION

Begin by constructing the finite difference table.

x_i	f_i	Δf_i	$\Delta^2 f_i$	$\Delta^3 f_i$	$\Delta^4 f_i$
-2	-27				
		23			
-1	-4		-18		
		5		12	
0	1		-6		0
		-1		12	
1	0		6		
		5			
2	5				

The value of h, the spacing of the x values, is 1.

The Newton interpolating polynomial is

$$f(x) = f_0 + \frac{x - x_0}{h}\Delta f_0 + \frac{(x - x_0)(x - x_1)}{2!h^2}\Delta^2 f_0 + \frac{(x - x_0)(x - x_1)(x - x_2)}{3!h^3}\Delta^3 f_0$$
$$+ \frac{(x - x_0)(x - x_1)(x - x_2)(x - x_3)}{4!h^4}\Delta^4 f_0.$$

Since $\Delta^4 f_0 = 0$, substituting $x = 1.21$ gives

$$f(x) = f_0 + \frac{x - x_0}{h}\Delta f_0 + \frac{(x - x_0)(x - x_1)}{2!h^2}\Delta^2 f_0 + \frac{(x - x_0)(x - x_1)(x - x_2)}{3!h^3}\Delta^3 f_0$$

$$= -27 + \left(\frac{1.21 - (-2)}{1} \times 23\right) + \left(\frac{(1.21 - (-2))(1.21 - (-1))}{2!1^2} \times (-18)\right)$$

$$+ \left(\frac{(1.21 - (-2))(1.21 - (-1))(1.21 - 0)}{3!1^3} \times 12\right)$$

> When you are trying to approximate $f(x)$ for a particular value of x, there is no need to simplify the interpolating polynomial itself.

$$= -27 + (3.21 \times 23) + \left[\left(\frac{3.21 \times 2.21}{2}\right) \times (-18)\right] + \left[\left(\frac{3.21 \times 2.21 \times 1.21}{6}\right) \times 12\right]$$

$$= -27 + 73.83 - 63.8469 + 17.167\,722$$

$$= 0.150\,822$$

$$= 0.151 \text{ to 3 decimal places.}$$

An alternative approach

The following method is due to Joseph Louis Lagrange. Notice that the points do not have to have equally spaced x values.

The function whose graph is a straight line which passes through the points (a, A) and (b, B) is

$$f(x) = \frac{A(x-b)}{a-b} + \frac{B(x-a)}{b-a} \qquad \text{provided } a \neq b.$$

 Why is the graph of the function above a straight line?
Substitute in the values $x = a$ and $x = b$ to check that $f(a) = A$ and $f(b) = B$.

The quadratic function whose graph passes through the points (a, A), (b, B) and (c, C) is

$$f(x) = \frac{A(x-b)(x-c)}{(a-b)(a-c)} + \frac{B(x-c)(x-a)}{(b-c)(b-a)} + \frac{C(x-a)(x-b)}{(c-a)(c-b)}$$

provided a, b and c are all different.

 Why is the graph of the function above a quadratic?
Substitute in the values $x = a$, $x = b$ and $x = c$ to check that $f(a) = A$, $f(b) = B$ and $f(c) = C$.

This pattern emerging here can be continued to deal with more points.

 Write down the cubic function whose graph passes through (a, A), (b, B), (c, C) and (d, D) where a, b, c and d are all different.

EXERCISE 4B

1 **(i)** Construct a finite difference table for the following data.
  (ii) What degree of polynomial is required to fit all seven data pairs?

x_i	1.20	1.25	1.30	1.35	1.40	1.45	1.50
f_i	29	6	0	0	0	−1	1

2 Find a polynomial which exactly fits the following data values.

x_i	2	5	8	11
f_i	7	16	25	34

3 Find a polynomial which exactly fits the following data values.

x_i	0	1	2	3
f_i	1	3	7	13

4 (i) Find a polynomial which exactly fits the following data values.

x_i	2	3	4	5
f_i	1	1	2	2

(ii) Use your polynomial to approximate f(4.1).

5 (i) Determine the degree of the polynomial of minimum degree which exactly fits the following data values.

x	0	1	2	3	4	5
$f(x)$	3	2	7	24	59	118

(ii) Use the Newton interpolation formula to estimate the value of f(3.2).

6 Use the following data to estimate the value of y at $x = 0.58$, using a cubic polynomial which fits the data exactly at $x = 0.3, 0.5, 0.7$ and 0.9.

x	0.1	0.3	0.5	0.7	0.9	1.1
$f(x)$	0.003	0.067	0.148	0.248	0.370	0.518

7 For each of the following, use Lagrange's method to find a function whose graph passes through the points given.
(i) (1, 4) and (2, 6)
(ii) (0, 1), (2, 3) and (3, 1)
(iii) (0, 1), (1, 4), (2, 15) and (3, 40)

8 The function f(x) is known to be a cubic.
Part of a difference table for f(x) is shown.

x_i	f_i	Δf_i	$\Delta^2 f_i$	$\Delta^3 f_i$
0				
1				
		7		6
2	19		−2	
3				
4				

(i) Copy and complete the difference table.

(ii) Use Newton's forward difference formula to obtain f(x), expressing your answer in the form $ax^3 + bx^2 + cx + d$.

(iii) Verify that the equation f(x) = 0 has a root at 0.15 correct to 2 decimal places.

(iv) Using the fact that Simpson's rule is exact for cubics, find, as efficiently as possible the exact value of $\int_0^4 f(x)\,dx$.

[MEI]

Truncating Newton's interpolating polynomial

Look at the following difference table.

x_i	f_i	Δf_i	$\Delta^2 f_i$	$\Delta^3 f_i$	$\Delta^4 f_i$
5	36.000 40				
		24.005 40			
7	60.005 80		8.031 91		
		32.037 31		0.102 10	
9	92.043 11		8.134 01		0.193 90
		40.171 32		0.296 00	
11	132.214 43		8.430 01		
		48.601 33			
13	180.815 76				

Since $\Delta^4 f_0 \neq 0$, a quartic is required for an exact fit.

However, the second differences column is roughly constant and so the third differences and onwards are nearly zero. This means that the interpolating polynomial used as far as the quadratic term will be a reasonably good fit. The technical term for the omission of terms from the end of a sum is *truncating*.

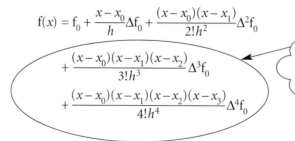

$$f(x) = f_0 + \frac{x - x_0}{h}\Delta f_0 + \frac{(x - x_0)(x - x_1)}{2!h^2}\Delta^2 f_0$$

$$+ \frac{(x - x_0)(x - x_1)(x - x_2)}{3!h^3}\Delta^3 f_0$$

$$+ \frac{(x - x_0)(x - x_1)(x - x_2)(x - x_3)}{4!h^4}\Delta^4 f_0$$

Since $\Delta^3 f_0$ and $\Delta^4 f_0$ are very small, if these terms are omitted, f(x) will no longer fit the data exactly but it should still be a good approximation.

The polynomial as far as the quadratic term is

$$f(x) = f_0 + \frac{x - x_0}{h}\Delta f_0 + \frac{(x - x_0)(x - x_1)}{2!h^2}\Delta^2 f_0$$

$$= 36.0004 + \frac{x - 5}{2} \times 24.0054 + \frac{(x - 5)(x - 7)}{8} \times 8.03191$$

$$= 1.00398875x^2 - 0.045165x + 11.12650625.$$

The values, to 4 decimal places, of this function at the values of x given are as follows.

x	5	7	9	11	13
f(x)	36.0004	60.0058	92.0431	132.1123	180.2135

These compare well to the original data which is reproduced below.

x_i	5	7	9	11	13
f_i	36.00040	60.00580	92.04311	132.21443	180.81576

Of course, if you needed to estimate the value of the function at 16.2, say, you can substitute $x = 16.2$ into the equation above for f(x).

EXAMPLE 4.5

What degree of polynomial is required for a good approximation to the following data values? Use this polynomial to approximate f(2.5).

x_i	0	1	2	3
f_i	10.0	13.2	17.9	24.6

SOLUTION

x_i	f_i	Δf_i	$\Delta^2 f_i$	$\Delta^3 f_i$
0	10.0			
		3.2		
1	13.2		1.5	
		4.7		0.1
2	17.9		1.6	
		6.3		
3	24.2			

Since the second differences are nearly constant, the quadratic approximation

$$f(x) = f_0 + \frac{x - x_0}{h}\Delta f_0 + \frac{(x - x_0)(x - x_1)}{2!h^2}\Delta^2 f_0$$

will be a good fit.

Using this to approximate f(2.5) gives

$$f(2.5) = 10 + \frac{2.5 - 0}{1} \times 3.2 + \frac{(2.5 - 0)(2.5 - 1)}{2} \times 1.5$$

$$= 20.8125.$$

Further points

When there is particular interest in the behaviour of the function around only *some* of the known *x* values it may not be necessary to calculate a polynomial which fits *all* the data points. Instead a polynomial of lesser degree which fits only the data points of interest may suffice.

So far, all the Newton interpolating polynomials have been calculated from the values f_0, Δf_0, $\Delta^2 f_0$, ... along the top diagonal of the difference table. Such interpolating polynomials are said to be *taken about x_0*.

It is possible to take an interpolating polynomial about x_1 or x_2 and so on.

For example, the interpolating polynomial about x_2 is given as follows.

$$f(x) = f_2 + \frac{x - x_2}{h}\Delta f_2 + \frac{(x - x_2)(x - x_3)}{2!h^2}\Delta^2 f_2 + \frac{(x - x_2)(x - x_3)(x - x_4)}{3!h^3}\Delta^3 f_2 + \dots$$

Notice that this is exactly the same formula as for the Newton interpolating polynomial except that all the subscripts have been increased by 2.

The values used in this formula are circled in the difference table below.

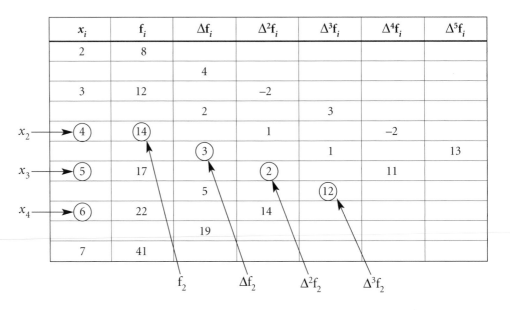

x_i	f_i	Δf_i	$\Delta^2 f_i$	$\Delta^3 f_i$	$\Delta^4 f_i$	$\Delta^5 f_i$
2	8					
		4				
3	12		−2			
		2		3		
x_2 → ④	⑭		1		−2	
		③		1		13
x_3 → ⑤	17		②		11	
		5		⑫		
x_4 → ⑥	22		14			
		19				
7	41					

$f_2 \qquad \Delta f_2 \qquad \Delta^2 f_2 \qquad \Delta^3 f_2$

So, for this set of data points, the Newton interpolating polynomial taken about x_2 is given by

$$f(x) = f_2 + \frac{x - x_2}{h}\Delta f_2 + \frac{(x - x_2)(x - x_3)}{2!h^2}\Delta^2 f_2 + \frac{(x - x_2)(x - x_3)(x - x_4)}{3!h^3}\Delta^3 f_2$$

$$= 14 + \frac{x - 4}{1} \times 3 + \frac{(x - 4)(x - 5)}{2!1^2} \times 2 + \frac{(x - 4)(x - 5)(x - 6)}{3!1^3} \times 12$$

$$= 2x^3 - 29x^2 + 142x - 218$$

You can check that this polynomial passes through the points $(4, 14)$, $(5, 17)$, $(6, 22)$ and $(7, 41)$ but not through the points $(2, 8)$ and $(3, 12)$. This is to be expected because the calculation carried out is exactly the one you would do for the interpolating polynomial of the four-point data set consisting of $(4, 14)$, $(5, 17)$, $(6, 22)$ and $(7, 41)$. The graph of the polynomial and the six data points are shown in figure 4.4.

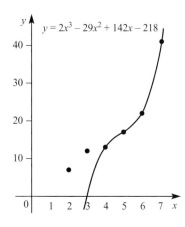

Figure 4.4

So the Newton interpolating polynomial based at x_i is only guaranteed to pass through the point (x_i, f_i) and those with larger x values.

Another technique you can use when circumstances allow is to simply truncate Newton's interpolating polynomial after a certain number of terms to make your calculations easier. The consequences of doing this must be understood.

- The earlier the polynomial is terminated, the fewer data points the resultant polynomial will pass through.

- The function may not be a good approximation of those data points it does not pass through and therefore it will not be a good approximation of the function at points nearby either.

The table gives the names and properties of various truncations of the Newton interpolating polynomial taken about x_0.

Truncated interpolating polynomial	Referred to as	Points it definitely passes through
$f(x) = f_0$	Constant approximation taken about x_0	(x_0, f_0) only
$f(x) = f_0 + \dfrac{x - x_0}{h} \Delta f_0$	Linear approximation taken about x_0	(x_0, f_0) and (x_1, f_1) only
$f(x) = f_0 + \dfrac{x - x_0}{h} \Delta f_0 + \dfrac{(x - x_0)(x - x_1)}{2!h^2} \Delta^2 f_0$	Quadratic approximation taken about x_0	$(x_0, f_0), (x_1, f_1)$ and (x_2, f_2) only
$f(x) = f_0 + \dfrac{x - x_0}{h} \Delta f_0 + \dfrac{(x - x_0)(x - x_1)}{2!h^2} \Delta^2 f_0$ $+ \dfrac{(x - x_0)(x - x_1)(x - x_2)}{3!h^2} \Delta^3 f_0$	Cubic approximation taken about x_0	$(x_0, f_0), (x_1, f_1),$ (x_2, f_2) and (x_3, f_3) only

Note

Linear interpolation is the term used when two data points (x_0, f_0) and (x_1, f_1) are available and the linear approximation based at x_0 is used to approximate the value of a function at a value x between x_0 and x_1.

EXERCISE 4C

1 For the following five points

$$A(0, 3), B(1, 13), C(2, 15), D(3, 8) \text{ and } E(4, 11)$$

find

(i) a quadratic passing through C, D and E

(ii) a cubic passing through B, C, D and E

(iii) a quadratic passing through A, C and E.

2 Consider the following data points.

x_i	0	1	2	3	4
f_i	7	10	9	14	14

Use each of the following polynomials to find approximations to f(3.5) and comment on your answers.
 (i)   The constant approximation taken about x_0
 (ii) The linear approximation taken about x_0
 (iii) The quadratic approximation taken about x_0
 (iv) The constant approximation taken about x_3
 (v)   The linear approximation taken about x_3
 (vi) The quadratic approximation taken about x_2

3 The table below shows some values, correct to 4 decimal places, of a function f(x).

x	0	1	2	3
f(x)	1.5557	1.0642	1.0154	1.3054

 (i)   Use a difference table to show that f(x) cannot be approximated well by a quadratic.
 (ii) Use Newton's interpolation formula to find, in the form $a + bx + cx^2 + dx^3$, the cubic function which passes through the data points.
       Hence estimate f(1.5) and f'(1.5)
 (iii) It is known that f(x) is never less than 1 for $0 \leqslant x \leqslant 3$.
       Discuss briefly the usefulness or otherwise of the approximating cubic found in part **(ii)**.

4 A function f(x) has values as shown in the table.

x	0	1	2	3	4	5
f(x)	0.2	1.8	6.1	14.2	27.3	46.6

 (i)   Show by means of a difference table, that f(x) appears to be approximated well by a cubic polynomial.
 (ii) Extend the difference table to give an estimate of f(6).
       Discuss briefly the reliability of this estimate.
 (iii) Use Newton's forward difference interpolation formula to estimate f(2.5).
       Comment on the reliability of this estimate.

[MEI, *part*]

5 In the difference table below, the values of x are exact but the values of $f(x)$ may be subject to error.

x_i	f_i	Δf_i	$\Delta^2 f_i$	$\Delta^3 f_i$	$\Delta^4 f_i$
0	1.77				
		1.87			
1	3.64		0.26		
		2.13		0.23	
2	5.77		0.49		0.18
		2.62		0.41	
3	8.39		0.90		
		3.52			
4	11.91				

(i) Use Newton's forward difference method to obtain a sequence of four estimates, linear, quadratic, cubic and quartic, for $f(0.8)$.

Assuming the values of $f(x)$ are exact, give an estimated value for $f(0.8)$ to the accuracy that appears justified.

(ii) Now assume that the values of $f(x)$ are rounded to 2 decimal places. Do you think your approximation for $f(0.8)$ is reliable? Give reasons for your answer.

[MEI]

KEY POINTS

1 Given values $f_0, f_1, f_2, f_3, ..., f_n$, the forward difference operator, Δ, is defined by
$$\Delta f_0 = f_1 - f_0, \qquad \Delta f_1 = f_2 - f_1 \quad \text{and so on.}$$

2 A finite difference table displays values of a function and their differences.

3 The nth differences of a polynomial with degree n are constant.

4 Newton's interpolating polynomial is given by

$$f(x) = f_0 + \frac{x - x_0}{h}\Delta f_0 + \frac{(x - x_0)(x - x_1)}{2!h^2}\Delta^2 f_0 + \frac{(x - x_0)(x - x_1)(x - x_2)}{3!h^3}\Delta^3 f_0 + \dots$$

Numerical differentiation

5

Small fleas have little fleas
Upon their back to bite 'em
And the little fleas have lesser fleas
And so *ad infinitum*.

Dean Swift

Sometimes a computer program may require the gradient of a function to carry out a calculation. In mathematics, the gradient is found by differentiation but the process of differentiation is not a natural one for a computer to perform other than for very simple functions. It may be easier for a computer to approximate the gradient rather than calculate an exact value through differentiation.

A good example of this is the Newton–Raphson method where the derivative of a function is required in the formula

$$x_{r+1} = x_r - \frac{f(x_r)}{f'(x_r)}.$$

The broad name for the topic in which numerical methods are used to approximate the gradient of a function is *numerical differentiation*.

The forward difference approximation

The gradient of the tangent to the curve at B in figure 5.1 can be seen to be reasonably approximated by the gradient of the chord BC. This is the straight line between $(x, f(x))$ and $(x + h, f(x + h))$.

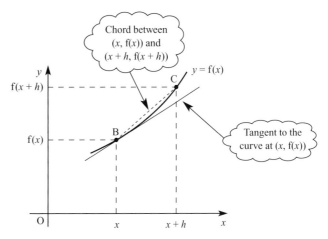

Figure 5.1

❓ What happens to the gradient of the chord as h is made smaller in figure 5.1?

The gradient of the chord is $\dfrac{f(x + h) - f(x)}{h}$. This gives the forward difference approximation to the derivative.

$$f'(x) \approx \frac{f(x + h) - f(x)}{h}.$$

❓ Why do you think this is called the 'forward' difference approximation?

EXAMPLE 5.1

For the function $f(x) = x^2 \sin x$, calculate the forward difference approximations to $f'(2)$ with $h = 0.1, 0.05, 0.025$ and 0.0125.

SOLUTION

The forward difference approximation to $f'(x)$ is given by

$$f'(x) \approx \frac{f(x + h) - f(x)}{h}.$$

In each case below $x = 2$.

With $h = 0.1$, this gives

$$f'(2) \approx \frac{f(2 + 0.1) - f(2)}{1}$$

$$= \frac{2.1^2 \sin 2.1 - 2^2 \sin 2}{0.1}$$

$$= 1.6956 \text{ (to 4 d.p.)}.$$

With $h = 0.05$,

$$f'(2) \approx \frac{f(2 + 0.05) - f(2)}{1}$$

$$= \frac{2.05^2 \sin 2.05 - 2^2 \sin 2}{0.05}$$

$$= 1.8390 \text{ (to 4 d.p.)}.$$

With $h = 0.025$,

$$f'(2) \approx \frac{f(2 + 0.025) - f(2)}{0.025}$$

$$= \frac{2.025^2 \sin 2.025 - 2^2 \sin 2}{0.025}$$

$$= 1.9070 \text{ (to 4 d.p.)}.$$

And with $h = 0.0125$,

$$f'(2) \approx \frac{f(2 + 0.0125) - f(2)}{0.0125}$$

$$= \frac{2.0125^2 \sin 2.0125 - 2^2 \sin 2}{0.0125}$$

$$= 1.9401 \text{ (to 4 d.p.).}$$

These approximations appear to be approaching a value slightly less than 2. This will be looked at in more detail in the next chapter.

The central difference approximation

In figure 5.2 the gradient of the chord CB and the gradient of the tangent at A appear to be almost the same.

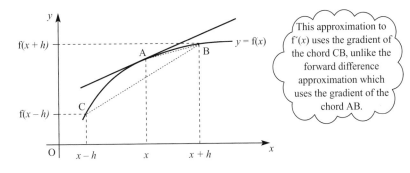

This approximation to f'(x) uses the gradient of the chord CB, unlike the forward difference approximation which uses the gradient of the chord AB.

Figure 5.2

The gradient of the chord is $\dfrac{f(x + h) - f(x - h)}{(x + h) - (x - h)}$. This gives the central difference approximation to the derivative.

$$f'(x) \approx \frac{f(x + h) - f(x - h)}{2h}.$$

EXAMPLE 5.2

For the function $f(x) = \sqrt{\cos x}$, calculate the central difference approximations to $f'(1)$ with $h = 0.2, 0.1$ and 0.05.

SOLUTION

The central difference approximation to $f'(x)$ is given by

$$f'(x) \approx \frac{f(x + h) - f(x - h)}{2h}.$$

In each case below $x = 1$.

With $h = 0.2$

$$f'(1) \approx \frac{f(1 + 0.2) - f(1 - 0.2)}{0.4}$$

$$= \frac{\sqrt{\cos 1.2} - \sqrt{\cos 0.8}}{0.4}$$

$$= -0.581\,82 \text{ (to 5 d.p.).}$$

With $h = 0.1$

$$f'(1) \approx \frac{f(1 + 0.1) - f(1 - 0.1)}{0.2}$$

$$= \frac{\sqrt{\cos 1.1} - \sqrt{\cos 0.9}}{0.2}$$

$$= -0.574\,64 \text{ (to 5 d.p.).}$$

With $h = 0.05$

$$f'(1) \approx \frac{f(1 + 0.05) - f(1 - 0.05)}{0.1}$$

$$= \frac{\sqrt{\cos 1.05} - \sqrt{\cos 0.95}}{0.1}$$

$$= -0.572\,594 \text{ (to 5 d.p.).}$$

EXAMPLE 5.3

Obtain approximations to the derivative of $f(x) = \sin x$ at $x = \frac{\pi}{4}$ using both the forward and central difference approximations with step sizes 0.2 and 0.1.

The exact value of the derivative at $x = \frac{\pi}{4}$ is 0.707 11 (to 5 decimal places). Use this value to calculate the absolute error in each approximation.

SOLUTION

Using the forward difference approximation with $h = 0.2$,

$$f'\left(\frac{\pi}{4}\right) \approx \frac{f\left(\frac{\pi}{4} + 0.2\right) - f\left(\frac{\pi}{4}\right)}{0.2} = 0.631\,93 \text{ (to 5 d.p.).}$$

With $h = 0.1$,

$$f'\left(\frac{\pi}{4}\right) \approx \frac{f\left(\frac{\pi}{4} + 0.1\right) - f\left(\frac{\pi}{4}\right)}{0.1} = 0.670\,60 \text{ (to 5 d.p.).}$$

Using the central difference formula with $h = 0.2$,

$$f'\left(\frac{\pi}{4}\right) \approx \frac{f\left(\frac{\pi}{4} + 0.2\right) - f\left(\frac{\pi}{4} + 0.2\right)}{0.4} = 0.702\,40 \text{ (to 5 d.p.).}$$

and with $h = 0.1$,

$$f'\left(\frac{\pi}{4}\right) \approx \frac{f\left(\frac{\pi}{4} + 0.1\right) - f\left(\frac{\pi}{4} - 0.1\right)}{0.2} = 0.705\,93 \text{ (to 5 d.p.)}.$$

Using $f'\left(\frac{\pi}{4}\right) = 0.707\,11$, the absolute errors are as given in the table.

	$h = 0.2$	$h = 0.1$
Forward difference	0.075 18	0.036 51
Central difference	0.004 71	0.001 18

As you would expect, for each formula, if the step size h is decreased, the error in the approximation is reduced. Also, the central difference formula gives a more accurate approximation than the corresponding forward difference formula.

Figure 5.3 shows the forward difference and the central difference approximation to the derivative $f'(x)$. Notice that, at least for the function with this graph, the central difference approximation appears to be more accurate than the forward difference approximation.

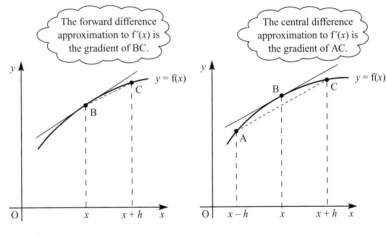

Figure 5.3

 Why would you expect the central difference approximation to be more accurate than the forward difference approximation in general?

Can you draw the graph of a function for which the forward difference approximation will be better than the central difference approximation to $f'(x)$ for some value of x and some value of h?

Calculating the error in f(x) when there is an error in x

Frequently, a value X is used as an approximation to an exact value x. You may wish to have an idea of the value of $f(x)$. It seems sensible to think about what happens if $f(X)$ is used as an approximation to $f(x)$.

For example, $X = 10$ could be used as an approximation to $x = 9.88$ in the function $f(x) = x^2$.

Then

$$f(X) = f(10) = 100$$

and

$$f(x) = f(9.88) = 97.6144.$$

So the error in $f(X)$ as an approximation to $f(x)$ is $100 - 97.6144 = 2.3856$. Compare this to the error of just 0.12 in the original approximation.

This can be illustrated with a diagram. The graph of $f(x) = x^2$ is shown in figure 5.4.

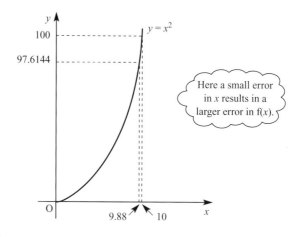

Figure 5.4

From this diagram you can see that the large error in $f(X)$ is due to the steep gradient of the function around $x = 9.88$.

The forward difference approximation can be used to explain this.

If X is an approximation to x with an error of h then $X - x = h$ or $X = x + h$.

The forward difference approximation to the derivative of a function f is, where h is small,

$$f'(x) \approx \frac{f(x + h) - f(x)}{h}.$$

Substituting $X = x + h$ gives,

$$f'(x) \approx \frac{f(X) - f(x)}{h}$$

or

$$f(X) - f(x) \approx f'(x)h.$$

Of course $f(X) - f(x)$ is the error when $f(X)$ is used as an approximation to $f(x)$ and so if the error in the approximation X of the exact value x is h then the error in the approximation $f(X)$ to $f(x)$ is approximately $f'(x)h$.

This is illustrated in the next example.

EXAMPLE 5.4

The function $f(x)$ is given by $f(x) = x^3$.
Calculate the error in approximating $f(5.92)$ by $f(X)$ in the cases when
(i) $X = 6.0$
(ii) $X = 5.9$.

In each case relate the answer to the derivative of $f(x)$.

SOLUTION

(i) The exact value of $f(5.92)$ is $5.92^3 = 207.474\,688$.

Using $X = 6.0$ gives $f(X) = 216$.
The error in this approximation of $f(5.92)$ is

$$f(6) - f(5.92) = 216 - 207.474\,688$$
$$= 8.525\,312.$$

The relationship with the derivative of f is that $f(X) - f(x) \approx f'(x)h$ where $h = X - x$.

In fact $\quad f'(x)h = 3 \times 5.92^2 \times (6 - 5.92)$
$$= 8.411\,136.$$

(ii) Using $X = 5.9$ gives $f(X) = 205.379$.
The error in this approximation of $f(5.92)$ is

$$f(5.9) - f(5.92) = 205.379 - 207.474\,688$$
$$= -2.095\,688.$$

This time $\quad h = 5.9 - 5.92$

and $\quad f'(x)h = 3 \times 5.92^2 \times (5.9 - 5.92)$

$$= -2.102\,784.$$

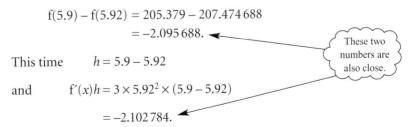

You can see that these two numbers are close.

These two numbers are also close.

1 Given that $f(x) = x^5$, obtain forward and central difference approximations to $f'(1)$ and $f'(1.5)$, taking $h = 0.2$, $h = 0.1$ and $h = 0.05$.

Calculate the exact value of $f'(1)$ by differentiating f and hence calculate the absolute error in each of your approximations.

Comment on the results.

2 Given that $f(x) = \cos(x)$, obtain forward and central difference approximations to $f'(0)$ and $f'(1.5)$, taking $h = 0.2$, $h = 0.04$ and $h = 0.008$.

Explain why the central difference formula performs so well in approximating $f'(0)$.

3 Given that $f(x) = \tan x$, where x is in radians, evaluate $f(x)$ for $x = 1.55$ and for $x = 1.56$.

Calculate the percentage change in $f(x)$ when x changes from $x = 1.55$ to $x = 1.56$ and compare this with the percentage change in the value of x.

Explain with a graph why the change in $f(x)$ is so large.

4 In this question $f(x) = x^x$.

   (i) Use your calculator to evaluate $f(x)$ at $x = 10^{-3}$, 10^{-5}, 10^{-7} and 10^{-9}.

   You are now given that $f(0) = 1$.

   (ii) Use the forward difference method with $h = 10^{-3}$ to estimate $f'(0)$.
   Obtain further estimates of $f'(0)$ by taking $h = 10^{-5}$, 10^{-7} and 10^{-9}.
   Comment on the sequence of estimates in relation to the likely value of $f'(0)$.

   (iii) A cheap calculator gives powers (such as x^x) rounded to 5 significant figures.
   What conclusions might be drawn by someone using such a calculator to carry out the processes in parts **(i)** and **(ii)**?

   What is the relevance of this result for more accurate calculators and computers?

5 The following five points lie on a curve $y = f(x)$.

$$(0, -1), (0.25, -0.9), (0.5, -1), (0.75, -1.1), (1, -1)$$

   (i) Obtain forward and central difference approximations to $f'(0.5)$ using the smallest values of h possible from the given information.

   (ii) Obtain, also, approximations to $f'(0.25)$ and $f'(0.75)$ and hence approximate $f''(0.5)$ using both forward and central differences.

   (iii) Comment on the values obtained.

1 The forward difference approximation to the derivative of a function f at a value x is given by

$$f'(x) \approx \frac{f(x+h) - f(x)}{h}$$

where h is small. By taking a series of approximations, making h smaller each time, it is possible to obtain a sequence of values which get closer and closer to the exact value of $f'(x)$.

2 The central difference approximation to the derivative of a function f at a value x is given by

$$f'(x) \approx \frac{f(x+h) - f(x-h)}{2h}$$

where h is small. By taking a series of approximations, making h smaller each time, it is possible to obtain a sequence of values which get closer and closer to the exact value of $f'(x)$.

3 If X is used as an approximation to x and the error is h (so that $X - x = h$) then the error when $f(X)$ is used as an approximation to $f(x)$, is approximately $f'(x)h$.

6 Rates of convergence in numerical processes

Are we nearly there yet?

Bart, The Simpsons

The sequences of numbers given in the table are correct to 14 decimal places.

n	a_n	b_n
0	2.000 000 000 000 00	2.000 000 000 000 00
1	1.587 401 051 968 20	1.733 333 333 333 33
2	1.736 665 658 837 39	1.699 395 733 136 02
3	1.685 693 436 581 69	1.698 885 603 631 44
4	1.703 443 962 965 84	1.698 885 489 846 34
5	1.697 304 622 708 76	1.698 885 489 846 33
6	1.699 433 044 142 72	1.698 885 489 846 33
7	1.698 695 754 833 64	1.698 885 489 846 33
8	1.698 951 225 723 47	1.698 885 489 846 33
9	1.698 862 713 709 11	1.698 885 489 846 33
10	1.698 893 381 169 68	1.698 885 489 846 33
11	1.698 882 755 696 41	1.698 885 489 846 33
12	1.698 886 437 160 14	1.698 885 489 846 33

Both sequences converge to the root, a, between $x = 1$ and $x = 2$, of the equation $x^3 + 3x - 10 = 0$. Figure 6.1 shows a graph of $f(x) = x^3 + 3x - 10$, on which a is marked. In fact a is exactly 1.698 885 489 846 33.

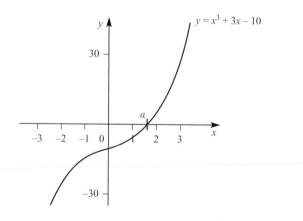

Figure 6.1

The sequence a_n was produced by taking $a_0 = 2$ and $a_{n+1} = \sqrt[3]{10 - 3a_n}$. Fixed point iteration was used as $x^3 + 3x - 10 = 0$ can be rearranged to $x = \sqrt[3]{10 - 3x}$.

The sequence b_n was produced by taking $b_0 = 2$ and $b_{n+1} = b_n - \left(\dfrac{b_n^3 + 3b_n - 10}{3b_n^2 + 3} \right)$ which is the iteration produced using the Newton–Raphson method. The table below shows the error in the terms listed above.

n	Error in a_n	Error in b_n
0	0.301 114 510 153 67	0.301 114 510 153 67
1	−0.111 484 437 878 13	0.034 447 843 487 00
2	0.037 780 168 991 06	0.000 510 243 289 69
3	−0.013 192 053 264 64	0.000 000 113 785 11
4	0.004 558 473 119 51	0.000 000 000 000 01
5	−0.001 580 867 137 57	0.000 000 000 000 00
6	0.000 547 554 296 39	0.000 000 000 000 00
7	−0.000 189 735 012 69	0.000 000 000 000 00
8	0.000 065 735 877 14	0.000 000 000 000 00
9	−0.000 022 776 137 22	0.000 000 000 000 00
10	0.000 007 891 323 35	0.000 000 000 000 00
11	−0.000 002 734 149 92	0.000 000 000 000 00
12	0.000 000 947 313 81	0.000 000 000 000 00

Studying the values in the table shows that the sequence b_n converges much more quickly to a than the sequence a_n.

In this chapter you will learn that it is possible to make ideas about the speed of convergence of sequences more precise. This will allow you to make better judgements about the relative merits of each method.

Rates of convergence of sequences

By using methods like Newton–Raphson or fixed point iteration, you have seen how to calculate sequences of values, $x_0, x_1, x_2, x_3, \ldots$, which converge to a root a of an equation.

Such a sequence is said to have *first-order convergence* if, for some fixed positive number k,

$$\frac{\text{absolute error in } x_1}{\text{absolute error in } x_0} \approx k, \frac{\text{absolute error in } x_2}{\text{absolute error in } x_1} \approx k, \frac{\text{absolute error in } x_3}{\text{absolute error in } x_2} \approx k, \ldots.$$

In other words, the absolute error in x_{n+1} is proportional to the absolute error in x_n.

? Why must the fixed positive number k in the description of first-order convergence on the previous page be less than 1?

A converging sequence is said to have *second-order convergence* if, for some fixed positive number k,

$$\frac{\text{absolute error in } x_1}{(\text{absolute error in } x_0)^2} \approx k, \quad \frac{\text{absolute error in } x_2}{(\text{absolute error in } x_1)^2} \approx k, \quad \frac{\text{absolute error in } x_3}{(\text{absolute error in } x_2)^2} \approx k, \dots.$$

In other words, the error in x_{n+1} is proportional to the square of the error in x_n.

? Does the value k have to be less than 1 in the definition of second-order convergence?

Higher-order convergence is defined similarly.

? What is the definition of third-order convergence?

The table below illustrates with examples how quickly absolute error decreases for each order of convergence. In each case the absolute error in the first term has been taken to be 0.1 and k has been taken to be 0.5.

Order of convergence	Absolute error in x_0	Absolute error in x_1	Absolute error in x_2	Absolute error in x_3
First	0.1	0.05	0.025	0.0125
Second	0.1	0.005	0.0000125	7.813×10^{-11}
Third	0.1	0.0005	6.25×10^{-11}	1.221×10^{-31}
Fourth	0.1	0.00005	3.125×10^{-18}	4.768×10^{-71}
Fifth	0.1	0.000005	1.563×10^{-27}	4.66×10^{-135}

You can see that, of these, first-order convergence is the slowest convergence (the absolute error reduces most slowly), with the speed of convergence increasing as the order of convergence increases.

Detecting first-order convergence in sequences

Usually, numerical methods are used in situations where it is not possible to obtain an exact value. An approximation is the best that can be hoped for. When it comes to looking for the order of convergence of a sequence this is a problem.

- The order of convergence of a sequence depends on the absolute error in each of its terms. The absolute error in a term, x_n, in a sequence converging to a is

$$\text{absolute error} = |x_n - a|.$$

- This cannot be calculated if the exact value of a is not available!

However, it is possible to detect first-order convergence by looking at the ratios of the differences between consecutive terms, namely

$$\frac{x_2 - x_1}{x_1 - x_0}, \frac{x_3 - x_2}{x_2 - x_1}, \frac{x_4 - x_3}{x_3 - x_2}, \dots$$

These values do not depend on a.

To illustrate this, take the example of the sequence $x_0 = 1$, $x_1 = 1.9$, $x_2 = 1.99$, $x_3 = 1.999$ and so on where the limit, $a = 2$, is known.

Notice that

$$\frac{\text{absolute error in } x_1}{\text{absolute error in } x_0} = \frac{x_1 - a}{x_0 - a} = \frac{|1.9 - 2|}{|1 - 2|} = 0.1$$

and $\frac{\text{absolute error in } x_2}{\text{absolute error in } x_1} = \frac{x_2 - a}{x_1 - a} = \frac{|1.99 - 2|}{|1.9 - 2|} = 0.1.$

 Confirm that the sequence has first-order convergence with $k = 0.1$ in the definition by calculating

$$\frac{\text{absolute error in } x_3}{\text{absolute error in } x_2} \text{ and } \frac{\text{absolute error in } x_4}{\text{absolute error in } x_3}.$$

The values $\frac{x_2 - x_1}{x_1 - x_0}, \frac{x_3 - x_2}{x_2 - x_1}, \dots$ are calculated in the following table.

n	x_n	$x_{n+1} - x_n$	$\dfrac{x_{n+2} - x_{n+1}}{x_{n+1} - x_n}$
0	1	0.9	0.1
1	1.9	0.09	0.1
2	1.99	0.009	0.1
3	1.999	0.0009	0.1

$\frac{x_2 - x_1}{x_1 - x_0} = \frac{1.99 - 1.9}{1.9 - 1} = \frac{0.09}{0.9} = 0.1$

$\frac{x_3 - x_2}{x_2 - x_1} = \frac{1.999 - 1.99}{1.99 - 1.9} = \frac{0.009}{0.09} = 0.1$

In this case at least, the ratios of differences between consecutive terms are the same as the value k in the definition of first-order convergence.

In general, if a sequence x_0, x_1, x_2, x_3, ... converging to a value a has first-order convergence then there is a fixed positive number k such that

$$\frac{\text{absolute error in } x_1}{\text{absolute error in } x_0} \approx k, \quad \frac{\text{absolute error in } x_2}{\text{absolute error in } x_1} \approx k, \quad \frac{\text{absolute error in } x_3}{\text{absolute error in } x_2} \approx k, \dots .$$

It turns out that for such a sequence the values

$$\frac{x_2 - x_1}{x_1 - x_0}, \frac{x_3 - x_2}{x_2 - x_1}, \frac{x_4 - x_3}{x_3 - x_2}, \dots$$

are all approximately equal to k or $-k$. This is explained below.

For an increasing sequence, x_0, x_1, x_2, x_3, ..., converging to a value a with first-order convergence if the absolute error in x_0 is ε, then the absolute error in x_1 is approximately $k\varepsilon$, where k is the number in the definition of first-order convergence.

You can see from figure 6.2 that

$$x_1 - x_0 \approx \varepsilon - k\varepsilon$$
$$= \varepsilon(1 - k).$$

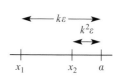

Figure 6.2

Similarly, since the absolute error in x_1 is approximately $k\varepsilon$, the absolute error in x_2 is approximately $k^2\varepsilon$.

You can see from figure 6.3 that

$$x_2 - x_1 \approx k\varepsilon - k^2\varepsilon$$
$$= k\varepsilon(1 - k).$$

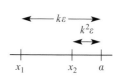

Figure 6.3

Therefore

$$\frac{x_2 - x_1}{x_1 - x_0} \approx \frac{k\varepsilon(1 - k)}{\varepsilon(1 - k)}$$
$$= k.$$

The same argument shows that

$$\frac{x_3 - x_2}{x_2 - x_1} \approx k, \quad \frac{x_4 - x_3}{x_3 - x_2} \approx k, \quad \frac{x_5 - x_4}{x_4 - x_3} \approx k, \text{ and so on.}$$

The value $\dfrac{x_{n+2} - x_{n+1}}{x_{n+1} - x_n}$ is sometimes referred to as the *ratio of differences*. It is the ratio of the differences between consecutives terms in a sequence.

ACTIVITY 6.1

Show that the ratios of differences behave similarly for the following two cases. You will find it useful to draw a diagram in each case.

1 A decreasing sequence $x_0, x_1, x_2, x_3, \ldots$ which converges to a with first-order convergence. You may find it useful to think about the example $x_0 = 3$, $x_1 = 2.1$, $x_2 = 2.01$, $x_3 = 2.0001$ and so on, which converges to $a = 2$.

2 A sequence that converges to a with first-order convergence and which alternates between being less than a and being greater than a. You may find it useful to think about the example $x_0 = 3$, $x_1 = 1.9$, $x_2 = 2.01$, $x_3 = 1.999$ and so on, which converges to $a = 2$.
In this case why would you expect the ratio of differences to be close to $-k$ rather than k as in the other two cases?

In the next example, first-order convergence is detected for a sequence with a limit that is not known.

EXAMPLE 6.1

Show, by considering ratios of differences, that the following sequence has first-order convergence.

Term	x_0	x_1	x_2	x_3	x_4	x_5
Value	0.38	0381672	0.381922955	0.381959726	0.381965094	0.381965877

SOLUTION

The ratios of differences are given in the table below.

> You can calculate the ratios of differences very quickly using a spreadsheet program.

n	x_n	$x_{n+1} - x_n$	$\dfrac{x_{n+2} - x_{n+1}}{x_{n+1} - x_n}$
0	0.38	0.001 672 000	0.150 092 703
1	0.381 672	0.000 250 955	0.146 524 277
2	0.381 922 955	0.000 036 771	0.145 984 607
3	0.381 959 726	0.000 005 368	0.145 864 382
4	0.381 965 094	0.000 000 783	
5	0.381 965 877		

The ratio of differences column, being nearly constant, provides evidence of first-order convergence.

EXAMPLE 6.2

The iteration $x_{r+1} = \cos x_r$ with $x_0 = 0.7$ gives a sequence which converges to a root a of the equation $\cos x = x$.

By considering x_0, x_1, x_2 and x_3, show that this iteration has first-order convergence.

SOLUTION

The first four terms in the sequence, x_0, x_1, x_2, x_3, are

$$0.7, 0.764\,842, 0.721\,492, 0.750\,821, \text{ respectively.}$$

The ratios of differences are

$$\frac{x_2 - x_1}{x_1 - x_0} = \frac{0.721\,492 - 0.764\,842}{0.764\,842 - 0.7}$$

$$= -0.668\,55$$

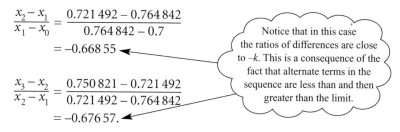

Notice that in this case the ratios of differences are close to $-k$. This is a consequence of the fact that alternate terms in the sequence are less than and then greater than the limit.

$$\frac{x_3 - x_2}{x_2 - x_1} = \frac{0.750\,821 - 0.721\,492}{0.721\,492 - 0.764\,842}$$

$$= -0.676\,57.$$

The fact that these two numbers are approximately the same indicates first-order convergence.

First-order convergence in fixed point iteration

A sequence x_0, x_1, x_2, ... is obtained from the iterative formula $x_{r+1} = g(x_r)$, with x_0 given. The function g has a fixed point at $x = a$.

Let $x_r = a + \varepsilon_r$

so that ε_r can be considered as the 'error' in the rth iterate.

Then, if the sequence converges to a, $\varepsilon_r \to 0$ as $r \to \infty$.

But $\quad x_{r+1} = g(x_r)$

so that $a + \varepsilon_{r+1} = g(a + \varepsilon_r)$. ①

From figure 6.4

$$g(a + \varepsilon_r) = PQ + QR$$
$$= g(a) + QR.$$

If ε_r is small,

$$\frac{QR}{SQ} \approx \text{slope of } y = g(x) \text{ at } x = a$$
$$\approx g'(a).$$

Therefore $\quad QR \approx \varepsilon_r g'(a)$

and from ①,

$$a + \varepsilon_{r+1} = g(a + \varepsilon_r)$$
$$= g(a) + \varepsilon_r g'(a).$$

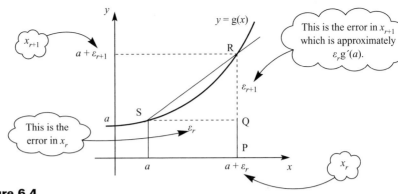

Figure 6.4

But, since a is a fixed point of g, $a = g(a)$ and hence

$$\varepsilon_{r+1} = \varepsilon_r g'(a). \qquad ②$$

So, the error at the $(r + 1)$th step is given, approximately, by the product of $g'(a)$ and the error at the rth step.

Since you are interested in the absolute error, note that from ②

$$|\varepsilon_{r+1}| = |g'(a)| \times |\varepsilon_r|$$

and hence $|\varepsilon_{r+1}| < |\varepsilon_r|$ if $|g'(a)| < 1$.

> This shows that this sequence has first-order convergence with the value $k = |g'(a)|$.

Therefore, if $|g'(a)| < 1$, the magnitude of the error in successive values of x_r will decrease and x_r will approach a as r tends to ∞.

Detecting second- or higher-order convergence in sequences

Second- or higher-order convergence is much faster than first-order and so you can get a very good approximation to the limit with only a few iterations. Since such an approximation is very close to the actual value of the limit you can use it to estimate closely the absolute error in each term.

It can be proved that, when the Newton–Raphson method produces a convergent sequence, that sequence has second-order convergence. The next example illustrates this.

EXAMPLE 6.3

Use the Newton–Raphson method with $x_0 = 1.5$ to find a root a of $x^2 - 2 = 0$ correct to 9 decimal places.
Use this to demonstrate that your sequence has second-order convergence.

SOLUTION

Let $f(x) = x^2 - 2$.

So $f'(x) = 2x$.

The sequence of iterations begins with $x_0 = 1.5$ and is generated by

$$x_{n+1} = x_n - \frac{f(x_n)}{f'(x_n)} = x_n - \left(\frac{x_n^2 - 2}{2x_n}\right).$$

The first six terms in the sequence are

1.5, 1.416 666 667, 1.414 215 686, 1.414 213 562, 1.414 213 562, 1.414 213 562

In fact $a = 1.414 213 562$ (to 9 d.p.).

Using $a = 1.414 213 562$ you can work out the absolute errors in the first few terms. They are approximately as follows.

> You can check this is true with a sign-change check: $f(1.414 213 561 5)$ is negative whilst $f(1.414 213 562 5)$ is positive. Notice how few iterations this took.

Absolute error in $x_0 \approx 1.5 - 1.414 213 562$
$$= 0.085 786 438$$

Absolute error in $x_1 \approx 1.414 666 667 - 1.414 213 562$
$$= 0.002 453 105$$

Absolute error in $x_2 \approx 1.414 215 686 - 1.414 213 562$
$$= 0.000 002 124$$

and then

$$\frac{\text{Absolute error in } x_1}{(\text{Absolute error in } x_0)^2} \approx \frac{0.002 453 105}{0.085 786 438^2} = 0.333 \text{ (to 3 d.p.)}$$

$$\frac{\text{Absolute error in } x_2}{(\text{Absolute error in } x_1)^2} \approx \frac{0.000 002 124}{0.002 453 105^2} = 0.353 \text{ (to 3 d.p.)}$$

These two numbers are about the same so it looks as though there is second-order convergence.

❓ Why is it impossible to approximate $\dfrac{\text{Absolute error in } x_3}{(\text{Absolute error in } x_2)^2}$ in the same way?

In summary,

- converging sequences produced by fixed point iteration generally have first-order convergence

- converging sequences produced by the Newton–Raphson method generally have second-order convergence.

Sometimes it is possible to get a good approximation of the limit of a sequence by considering how the terms in the sequence are approaching it. This will be considered later in the chapter.

EXERCISE 6A

1 By considering the ratios of differences, show that each of the following convergent sequences has first-order convergence.
   (i) $x_0 = 1$, $x_1 = 1.2$, $x_2 = 1.22$, $x_3 = 1.222$, $x_4 = 1.2222$, ...
   (ii) $x_0 = 8$, $x_1 = 7$, $x_2 = 6.5$, $x_3 = 6.25$, $x_4 = 6.125$, ...

(iii) $x_0 = 8$, $x_1 = 7$, $x_2 = 7.5$, $x_3 = 7.25$, $x_4 = 7.375$, ...

(iv) $x_0 = 3$, $x_1 = 2$, $x_2 = 1.732\,051$, $x_3 = 1.652\,892$, $x_4 = 1.628\,77$, ...

(v) $x_0 = 3$, $x_1 = 1.414\,213\,562$, $x_2 = 1.246\,504\,703$,
$x_3 = 1.224\,268\,944$, $x_4 = 1.221\,228\,201$, ...

2 By considering ratios of differences, show that the sequence given by $x_0 = 2$ and $x_{r+1} = \sqrt[4]{x_r^2 + 1}$ has first-order convergence.

3 By considering ratios of differences, show that the sequence given by $x_0 = 2.41$ and $x_{r+1} = 2 + \dfrac{1}{x_r}$ has first-order convergence.

What is the connection between the value of the ratios of differences and the derivative of $f(x) = 2 + \dfrac{1}{x}$?

4 Show that the following sequences have second-order convergence.

In each case the values given are, respectively, x_0, x_1, x_2 and so on.

(i) 1.5, 1.422619048, 1.414303964, 1.414213573, 1.414213562, 1.414213562, ...

(ii) 1.5, 1.254310345, 1.172277657, 1.164110042, 1.164035147, 1.164035147, ...

(iii) 1, 0.958585574, 0.958251921, 0.958251898, 0.958251898, 0.958251898, ...

(iv) 0, −0.2, −0.192613611, −0.192603672, −0.192603672, ...

Rates of convergence in methods of numerical integration and differentiation as *h* changes

In methods of numerical integration and differentiation, as h is reduced the resultant approximations get closer to the exact value. In this section the rate at which such approximations approach the exact value is considered.

Numerical integration

Look at the tables below.

	Approximation	h	Absolute error	(Absolute error) $\div h$	(Absolute error) $\div h^2$	(Absolute error) $\div h^3$	(Absolute error) $\div h^4$
M_2	0.800 781 250	0.5	0.199 218 750	0.398 438	0.796 875	1.593 750	3.187 500
M_4	0.948 486 328	0.25	0.051 513 672	0.206 055	0.824 219	3.296 875	13.187 500
M_8	0.987 014 771	0.125	0.012 985 229	0.103 882	0.831 055	6.648 438	53.187 520
T_2	1.406 250 000	0.5	0.406 250 000	0.812 500	1.625 000	3.250 000	6.500 000
T_4	1.103 515 625	0.25	0.103 515 625	0.414 063	1.656 250	6.625 000	26.500 000
T_8	1.026 000 977	0.125	0.026 000 977	0.208 008	1.664 063	13.312 500	106.500 000
S_2	1.002 604 167	0.5	0.002 604 167	0.005 208	0.010 417	0.020 833	0.041 667
S_4	1.000 162 760	0.25	0.000 162 760	0.000 651	0.002 604	0.010 417	0.041 667
S_8	1.000 010 173	0.125	0.000 010 173	0.000 081	0.000 651	0.005 208	0.041 669

The table on the left on the previous page shows values obtained using the mid-point rule, the trapezium rule and Simpson's rule to approximate the integral $\int_0^1 5x^4 dx$. The exact value of this integral can be easily calculated and is 1, so it is possible to calculate the absolute error in each estimate. These are contained in the table on the right along with their values after division by various powers of h.

Note

This integral has been chosen because its exact value is available to us, which means that the error in each approximation can be calculated exactly and the rate of convergence can be analysed. Usually a numerical method would only be used in a situation where it is difficult or impossible to find the exact value of the integral.

The values in the shaded cells are almost constant. This suggests that

- the absolute error in the mid-point and the trapezium rule is proportional to h^2

- the absolute error in Simpson's rule is proportional to h^4.

In fact, these results hold for most functions you will ever encounter.

The error in the mid-point rule and the trapezium rule

In the mid-point rule, the absolute error is proportional to h^2. In other words there is a constant k such that

$$\text{absolute error} = kh^2.$$

The power of h in this expression explains why the mid-point rule is described as a *second-order method*.

⚠ Do not confuse this with second-order convergence of sequences discussed earlier in this chapter; they are completely different concepts.

Two successive mid-point estimates to an integral are taken, the first using n strips and the second using $2n$ strips. If, when using n strips, the strip width is h then, when using $2n$ strips, the strip width will be $\frac{h}{2}$. Therefore

$$\text{Absolute error in } M_n \approx kh^2$$

and

$$\text{Absolute error in } M_{2n} \approx k\left(\frac{h}{2}\right)^2 = \frac{kh^2}{4}.$$

This means that halving h, or, equivalently, doubling n will reduce the absolute error in the subsequent approximation by a factor of 0.25.

Using the trapezium rule, the absolute error is proportional to h^2. Again it is a second-order method and, as with the mid-point rule, doubling n will reduce the absolute error by a factor of 0.25.

The error in Simpson's rule

In Simpson's rule, the absolute error is proportional to h^4. The power of h explains why Simpson's rule is described as a *fourth-order method*.

When two Simpson's rule estimates, S_n and S_{2n}, are taken to an integral

$$\text{Absolute error in } S_n = kh^4$$

and

$$\text{Absolute error in } S_{2n} = k\left(\frac{h}{2}\right)^4 = \frac{kh^4}{16}.$$

This means that halving h, or, equivalently, doubling n will reduce the absolute error by a factor of $\frac{1}{16} = 0.0625$.

Viewing error in terms of the ratio of differences

With doubling values of n, the factor by which the absolute error reduces in each method is the same as the 'ratio of differences' between successive estimates. The table below shows this for the integral considered above.

	Approximation	Difference	Ratio of differences
M_2	0.800 781 250		
M_4	0.948 486 328	0.147 705	
M_8	0.987 014 771	0.038 528	0.260 847
T_2	1.406 250 000		
T_4	1.103 515 625	−0.302 734	
T_8	1.026 000 977	−0.077 515	0.256 048
S_2	1.002 604 167		
S_4	1.000 162 760	−0.002 441	
S_8	1.000 010 173	−0.000 153	0.062 500

This number is $\dfrac{M_8 - M_4}{M_4 - M_2}$. It is very close to 0.25.

Close to 0.25.

Close to 0.0625.

Why does this happen? It is an identical situation to the one for first-order convergence in sequences.

Each successive approximation, where the number of strips is doubled, is four times as close to the exact value I as the previous one.

$$\frac{\text{Absolute error in } T_2}{\text{Absolute error in } T_1} \approx \frac{1}{4}, \frac{\text{Absolute error in } T_4}{\text{Absolute error in } T_2} \approx \frac{1}{4}, \frac{\text{Absolute error in } T_8}{\text{Absolute error in } T_4} \approx \frac{1}{4}, \dots .$$

This means, rather confusingly, that the sequence $T_1, T_2, T_4, T_8, \dots$ has first-order convergence with $k = 0.25$.

Also, for a convex or a concave area, such a sequence of estimates is either increasing or decreasing. You saw earlier how for such a sequence

$$\frac{T_4 - T_2}{T_2 - T_1} \approx \frac{1}{4}, \frac{T_8 - T_4}{T_4 - T_2} \approx \frac{1}{4}, \dots.$$

❓ Why should the ratio of differences between Simpson's rule approximations obtained by doubling n be close to $\frac{1}{16} = 0.0625$?

Extrapolated estimates

Take the example of the trapezium rule. It has been shown that the ratio of differences between estimates obtained by doubling the number of trapezia is around $\frac{1}{4}$. If you have calculated T_1, T_2, T_4 and T_8 then you would expect that

$$\frac{T_2 - T_1}{T_4 - T_2} \approx \frac{1}{4} \quad \text{and} \quad \frac{T_4 - T_2}{T_8 - T_4} \approx \frac{1}{4}.$$

⚠ There will be exceptions to this, especially when the early approximations T_1 and T_2 are particularly crude. It may be that this pattern only emerges for later estimates, for example when T_1, T_2, T_4 and T_8 are replaced by T_8, T_{16}, T_{32} and T_{64}, respectively.

This is shown in the number line in figure 6.5 for an increasing sequence, T_1, T_2, T_4, T_8, ...

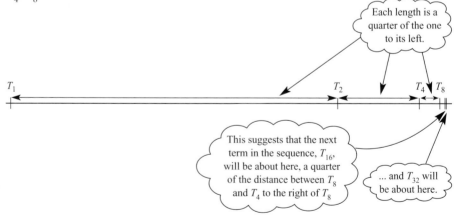

Figure 6.5

This prediction of the value of T_{16} can also be derived algebraically. If you were to go on and calculate T_{16} then you would also expect that

$$\frac{T_{16} - T_8}{T_8 - T_4} \approx \frac{1}{4}.$$

Rearranging this expression gives

$$T_{16} - T_8 \approx \frac{1}{4} \times (T_8 - T_4)$$

$$\Rightarrow \qquad T_{16} \approx T_8 + \frac{T_8 - T_4}{4}$$

So T_{16} should be approximately

$$T_8 + \frac{T_8 - T_4}{4}.$$

> It is certainly a lot easier to calculate this value than to do all the calculations involved in obtaining the actual value of T_{16}!

This value can be calculated as soon as T_4 and T_8 are known.

A value calculated like this is called an *extrapolated value* as it is obtained by considering what would happen if the pattern observed in the ratios of differences were to continue.

This extrapolated value of T_{16} could be used in the formula $T_{32} \approx T_{16} + \frac{T_{16} - T_8}{4}$

to get an extrapolated value of T_{32}. You can express this in terms of T_8 and T_4 as follows.

$$T_8 + \frac{T_8 - T_4}{4} + \frac{T_8 - T_4}{4^2}$$

You may see a pattern emerging here. The extrapolated value of T_{64} found similarly is given by

$$T_8 + \frac{T_8 - T_4}{4} + \frac{T_8 - T_4}{4^2} + \frac{T_8 - T_4}{4^3}.$$

There is nothing special about T_8 and T_4 in this discussion, extrapolated values beginning with any two consecutive estimates, T_n and T_{2n}, can be calculated.

Extrapolations to infinity!

Looking at the formulae for consecutive extrapolated values seen above it becomes apparent that successive extrapolated estimates are converging towards the value of the following series.

$$T_8 + \frac{T_8 - T_4}{4} + \frac{T_8 - T_4}{4^2} + \frac{T_8 - T_4}{4^3} + \frac{T_8 - T_4}{4^4} + \dots$$

The value of this infinite series can be calculated. It is T_8 plus a geometric series with a common ratio of 0.25. One way to do this is shown below.

$$T_8 + \frac{T_8 - T_4}{4} + \frac{T_8 - T_4}{4^2} + \frac{T_8 - T_4}{4^3} + \frac{T_8 - T_4}{4^4} + \dots$$

$$= T_8 + (T_8 - T_4)\left(\frac{1}{4} + \frac{1}{4^2} + \frac{1}{4^3} + \frac{1}{4^4} + \dots\right)$$

$$= T_8 + (T_8 - T_4) \frac{\frac{1}{4}}{1 - \frac{1}{4}}$$

$$= T_8 + (T_8 - T_4) \frac{\frac{1}{4}}{\frac{3}{4}}$$

$$= T_8 + \frac{T_8 - T_4}{3}$$

> Since the sum of the geometric series
> $$a + ar + ar^2 + \dots \text{ is } \frac{a}{1 - r}$$
> when $|r| < 1$.

EXAMPLE 6.4

The trapezium rule estimates to an integral are $T_2 = 2$, $T_4 = 1.81$ and $T_8 = 1.7652$.

By considering the ratio between the differences in successive estimates, give the value of the integral to the number of decimal places you feel is justified.

SOLUTION

The ratio of differences is

$$\frac{T_8 - T_4}{T_4 - T_2} = \frac{1.7652 - 1.81}{1.81 - 2}$$

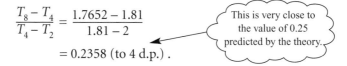

This is very close to the value of 0.25 predicted by the theory.

$$= 0.2358 \text{ (to 4 d.p.)} .$$

The extrapolated value of T_{16} is

$$T_8 + \frac{T_8 - T_4}{4} = 1.7652 + \frac{1.7652 - 1.81}{4}$$

$$= 1.754.$$

The extrapolated value of T_{32} is

$$T_8 + \frac{T_8 - T_4}{4} + \frac{T_8 - T_4}{4^2} = 1.7652 + \frac{1.7652 - 1.81}{4} + \frac{1.7652 - 1.81}{4^2}$$

$$= 1.7512.$$

The value of the series $T_8 + \dfrac{T_8 - T_4}{4} + \dfrac{T_8 - T_4}{4^2} + \dfrac{T_8 - T_4}{4^3} + \dfrac{T_8 - T_4}{4^4} + \dots$ is

$$1.7652 + \frac{1.7652 - 1.81}{4} + \frac{1.7652 - 1.81}{4^2} + \frac{1.7652 - 1.81}{4^3} + \dots$$

$$= 1.7652 + (1.7652 - 1.81)\left(\frac{1}{4} + \frac{1}{4^2} + \frac{1}{4^3} + \frac{1}{4^4} + \dots\right)$$

$$= 1.7652 + (1.7652 - 1.81)\left(\frac{\frac{1}{4}}{1 - \frac{1}{4}}\right)$$

$$= 1.7652 + \frac{1.7652 - 1.81}{3}$$

$$= 1.750\,267 \text{ (to 6 d.p.)}.$$

Comparing these values, it looks as though the estimate of 1.75 is correct to 2 d.p.

❓ Suppose that you have calculated the Simpson's rule estimates, S_{16} and S_{32}, as approximations to an integral.

1 What is the formula for the extrapolated value of S_{64} in terms of S_{16} and S_{32}?

2 What is the formula for the extrapolated value of S_{128} in terms of S_{16} and S_{32}?

3 What is the formula for the value that the sequence of extrapolations is converging to?

EXAMPLE 6.5

The Simpson's rule estimates to an integral are $S_1 = 1.3$, $S_2 = 1.3501$ and $S_4 = 1.353\,225$.

By considering the ratio between the differences in successive estimates, give the value of the integral to the number of decimal places you feel is justified.

SOLUTION

The ratio of differences is

$$\frac{S_4 - S_2}{S_2 - S_1} = \frac{1.353\,225 - 1.3501}{1.3501 - 1.3}$$

$$= \frac{0.003\,155}{0.0501}$$

> This is very close to the value of $\frac{1}{16} = 0.0625$ predicted by the theory.

$$= 0.0624 \text{ (to 4 d.p.)}.$$

Assuming this pattern continues

$$\frac{S_8 - S_4}{S_4 - S_2} \approx \frac{1}{16}$$

$$\Rightarrow \qquad S_8 \approx S_4 + \frac{S_4 - S_2}{16}$$

$$= 1.353\,225 + \frac{1.353\,225 - 1.3501}{16}$$

$$= 1.353\,420\,313.$$

The value obtained by summing the infinite series is

$$S_4 + \frac{S_4 - S_2}{16} + \frac{S_4 - S_2}{16^2} + \frac{S_4 - S_2}{16^3} + \dots$$

$$= S_4 + (S_4 - S_2)\left(\frac{1}{16} + \frac{1}{16^2} + \frac{1}{16^3} + \dots\right)$$

$$= S_4 + (S_4 - S_2)\left(\frac{\frac{1}{16}}{1 - \frac{1}{16}}\right)$$

$$= S_4 + \frac{S_4 - S_2}{15}$$

$$= 1.353\,225 + \frac{1.353\,225 - 1.3501}{15}$$

$$= 1.353\,433\,333$$

As these values agree to 4 decimal places, it seems reasonable to say that 1.353 is an approximation to the integral which is correct to 3 decimal places.

1 In each case, calculate the ratio of the differences between successive approximations to show that the estimates are consistent with the usual order of convergence in the method used.

(i) $T_1 = 10.0021$ $T_2 = 8.9979$, $T_4 = 8.7479$

(ii) $M_2 = 23.4623$, $M_4 = 25.4578$, $M_8 = 25.9432$

(iii) $S_1 = 34.1251$, $S_2 = 33.1249$, $S_4 = 33.0623$

2 In each case, some approximations are given in the usual notation, to an integral with an exact value of I.

By extrapolating from these approximations, using the usual order of convergence in the method used, give the value of I to a level of accuracy you feel is justified.

(i) $T_2 = 4.02341$, $T_4 = 4.09123$

(ii) $M_8 = 11.3421$, $M_{16} = 10.6745$

(iii) $S_1 = 4.5692$, $S_2 = 4.9899$

3 (i)   Find, in terms of a, the value of the integral $I = \int_0^a x^2 dx$.

Hence find the error in each of the following approximations to I.

(a) T_1, the value given by a single application of the trapezium rule

(b) M_1, the value given by a single application of the mid-point rule

Find the value of S_1, where $S_1 = \frac{1}{3}(T_1 + 2M_1)$, and comment.

(ii) For the integral $J = \int_{0.2}^1 \frac{1}{\sqrt{1 + x^3}} dx$, find the values of T_1 and M_1.

Hence find an improved estimate, S_1.

Find also the values of the estimates T_2, M_2 and S_2, where $S_2 = \frac{1}{3}(T_2 + 2M_2)$.

Hence give the value of J to the accuracy which is justified by your working.

Rates of convergence in methods of numerical differentiation

The table shows forward and central difference approximations to $f'(0)$ for the function $f(x) = x^2 + \sin x$.

h	Forward difference approximation to $f'(0)$	Central difference approximation to $f'(0)$
0.5	1.458 851 077	0.958 851 077
0.25	1.239 615 837	0.989 615 837
0.125	1.122 397 867	0.997 397 867
0.062 5	1.061 849 085	0.999 349 085
0.031 25	1.031 087 248	0.999 837 248
0.015 625	1.015 584 310	0.999 959 310

The exact value of f′(0) is 1 and the error in each approximation is shown in the tables below.

Forward difference approximation		
h	Error	Error ÷ h
0.5	0.458 851	0.917 702
0.25	0.239 616	0.958 463
0.125	0.122 398	0.979 183
0.062 5	0.061 849	0.989 585
0.031 25	0.031 087	0.994 792
0.015 625	0.015 584	0.997 396

For the forward difference approximation, Error ÷ h remains fairly constant indicating that the error is proportional to h.

Central difference approximation		
h	Error	Error ÷ h^2
0.5	−0.041 15	−0.164 60
0.25	−0.010 38	−0.166 15
0.125	−0.002 60	−0.166 54
0.062 5	−0.000 65	−0.166 63
0.031 25	−0.000 16	−0.166 66
0.015 625	−0.000 04	−0.166 66

For the central difference approximation, Error ÷ h^2 remains fairly constant indicating that the error is proportional to h^2.

These observations are true in general.

- For forward difference approximations, the error is proportional to h. It is referred to as a first-order method. Each time h is halved the error is approximately halved.

- For central difference approximations, the error is proportional to h^2. It is referred to as a second-order method. Each time h is halved, the error is approximately quartered.

- For the forward difference method, the ratio of differences between estimates obtained by repeatedly halving n, is around 0.5.

- For the central difference method, the ratio of differences is around 0.25.

The next two examples show how this can be used to give approximations to derivatives.

EXAMPLE 6.6

The table shows forward difference approximations to the gradient of a function at a value c.

h	0.1	0.05	0.025
Forward difference approximation	3.5101	3.2605	3.1298

Use these values to give an approximation to the value of the gradient at c correct to as many decimal places as you think are reliable.

SOLUTION

Looking at the ratio of differences between successive estimates, obtained upon halving h gives

$$\frac{3.1298 - 3.2605}{3.2605 - 3.5101} = 0.5236 \text{ (to 4 d.p.)}.$$

This is close to 0.5, as is expected for a first-order method such as the forward difference method.

Assuming that this pattern continues the extrapolated estimate for $h = 0.0125$ is

$$3.1298 + \frac{3.1298 - 3.2605}{2} = 3.064\,45.$$

The extrapolated estimate for $h = 0.00625$ is

$$3.1298 + \frac{3.1298 - 3.2605}{2} + \frac{3.1298 - 3.2605}{2^2} = 3.031\,775.$$

This sequence of extrapolated estimates tends to

$$3.1298 + \frac{3.1298 - 3.2605}{2} + \frac{3.1298 - 3.2605}{2^2} + \frac{3.1298 - 3.2605}{2^3} + \frac{3.1298 - 3.2605}{2^4} + \ldots$$

$$= 3.1298 + (3.1298 - 3.2605)\left(\frac{1}{2} + \frac{1}{2^2} + \frac{1}{2^3} + \frac{1}{2^4} + \ldots\right)$$

$$= 3.1298 + (3.1298 - 3.2605)\left(\frac{\frac{1}{2}}{1 - \frac{1}{2}}\right)$$

$$= 3.1298 + (3.1298 - 3.2605)\frac{\frac{1}{2}}{\frac{1}{2}}$$

$$= 3.1298 + (3.1298 - 3.2605) = 2.9991$$

Looking at these values, it looks as though the approximation 3.0 will be correct to 1 decimal place.

1 Forward difference approximations to the gradient of a function given for
$h = 0.1$, $h = 0.05$ and $h = 0.025$ are 5.201 001, 5.098 010 and 5.048 002
respectively.
Use extrapolation to give the value of the gradient to the level of accuracy you
think is reliable.

2 Central difference approximations to the gradient of a function given for
$h = 0.5$, $h = 0.25$ and $h = 0.125$ are 1.299 79, 1.199 99 and 1.174 989 respectively.
Use extrapolation to give the value of the gradient to the level of accuracy you
think is reliable.

3 A function f(x) has the values shown in the table. The values of x are exact; the
values of f(x) are correct to 5 decimal places.

x	1.6	1.8	1.9	2.0	2.1	2.2	2.4
f(x)	0.756 09	0.782 00	0.794 66	0.807 11	0.819 34	0.831 35	0.854 71

(i) Obtain three estimates of f′(2) using the forward difference method with h
taking values 0.4, 0.2, 0.1.
Show that, as h is halved, the differences between the estimates are
approximately halved.
Hence obtain the best estimate you can of f′(2).

(ii) Obtain three estimates of f′(2) using the central difference method.
Investigate how the differences between the estimates behave as h is halved.
Hence obtain the best estimate you can of f′(2).

(iii) Suppose now that estimates of f′(1.8) and f′(1.6) are required.
Without doing any calculations, state, with reasons, which of these two
methods you would use in each case.

4 The derivative of a function f(x) is being found numerically.

(i) The forward difference formula is used at $x = 3$ with values of h as shown
in the table.

h	0.1	0.05	0.025	0.0125
Estimate of f′(3)	5.7413	5.6424	5.5935	5.5693

By considering the differences between estimates, obtain the best estimate
you can of f′(3).
Give your answer correct to the number of significant figures to which you
consider it to be accurate. Explain your reasoning.

(ii) The central difference formula is used to estimate $f'(4)$.

h	0.1	0.05	0.025
Estimate of $f'(4)$	11.099 238	11.092 575	11.090 910

Obtain the best estimate you can of $f'(4)$.
Give your answer correct to the number of significant figures to which you consider it to be accurate.
Explain your reasoning.

(iii) By reference to your work in parts **(i)** and **(ii)**, describe the relative rates of convergence of the forward and central difference methods.

[MEI]

5 A function $f(x)$ has values as given in the following table.

x	0	0.2	0.4	0.6	0.8
$f(x)$	0	0.4199	0.6033	0.7598	0.9160

(i) Use Simpson's rule with $h = 0.4$ to find an estimate of $\int_0^{0.8} f(x)\, dx$.

Find a further estimate using Simpson's rule with $h = 0.2$.
Hence obtain the best estimate you can of the value of the integral.
Give your answer to the number of significant figures you can justify.

(ii) Use the central difference formula with two different values of h to find estimates of $f'(0.4)$.
Hence obtain the best estimate you can of the value of the derivative.
Give your answer to the number of significant figures you can justify.

[MEI]

KEY POINTS

1 Converging sequences can converge to their limits at different rates.

2 A sequence, $x_0, x_1, x_2, x_3, \ldots$, is said to have *first-order convergence* if, for some fixed positive number k,

$$\frac{\text{absolute error in } x}{\text{absolute error in } x_0} \approx k, \quad \frac{\text{absolute error in } x_2}{\text{absolute error in } x_1} \approx k, \quad \frac{\text{absolute error in } x_3}{\text{absolute error in } x_2} \approx k, \ldots.$$

In other words, the absolute error in x_{n+1} is proportional to the absolute error in x_n.

3 If a sequence has first-order convergence then the ratios of differences,

$$\frac{x_2 - x_1}{x_1 - x_0}, \frac{x_3 - x_2}{x_2 - x_1}, \frac{x_4 - x_3}{x_3 - x_2}, \ldots$$

are also all approximately equal, to k or $-k$.

4 A converging sequence is said to have *second-order convergence* if, for some fixed positive number k,

$$\frac{\text{absolute error in } x_1}{(\text{absolute error in } x_0)^2} \approx k, \frac{\text{absolute error in } x_2}{(\text{absolute error in } x_1)^2} \approx k,$$

$$\frac{\text{absolute error in } x_3}{(\text{absolute error in } x_2)^2} \approx k, \dots.$$

In other words, the error in x_{n+1} is proportional to the square of the error in x_n.

Higher-order convergence is defined similarly.

5 Second-order convergence is quicker and so it takes fewer iterations to get a good approximation to the limit. This can be used to get an approximation of the error in earlier iterations.

6 Converging sequences produced by fixed point iteration generally have first-order convergence.

7 Converging sequences produced by the Newton–Raphson method generally have second-order convergence.

8 In the mid-point rule and the trapezium rule, the absolute error is proportional to h^2. In other words there is a constant k such that

$$\text{absolute error} = kh^2.$$

The mid-point rule and the trapezium rule are said to be second-order methods, because of the power of h in this expression.

9 In Simpson's rule, the absolute error is proportional to h^4. Simpson's rule is said to be a fourth-order method.

10 When using the mid-point rule, the trapezium rule or Simpson's rule and doubling n or when taking forward difference or central difference approximations and halving h, the ratio of differences between successive estimates can be used to obtain a sequence of extrapolated estimates. These converge to a value which can be calculated.

Answers

Note: All answers are given to an appropriate degree of accuracy.

All answers will depend on the calculation procedures used; this should be taken into account when checking your answers.

Chapter 1

❓ (Page 1)

The number looks as though it has been rounded to the nearest thousand, although of course you cannot be certain of this.

❓ (Page 8)

(i)   0.05

(ii) 0.005

(iii) 0.5×10^{-n}

(iv) No it isn't. For example, the absolute error incurred when 350 is rounded to two significant figures is 50 whereas the absolute error incurred when 3500 is rounded to two significant figures is 500.

Exercise 1A (Page 8)

1

2 (i)   (a) 0.016

      (b) 0.0156

  (ii) (a) 0.010

      (b) 0.009 90

 (iii) (a) 2.667

      (b) 2.67

 (iv) (a) 3.571

      (b) 3.57

3 (i)   0.0125

  (ii) 28 420

 (iii) 110

 (iv) 91.49

 (v)   7.4300

 (vi) 0.001 42

4 (i)   3608

  (ii) −392

 (iii) 8

 (iv) −2

5 (i)   −0.010 050 506 3

  (ii) −0.002 979 438 5

 (iii) −0.000 151 011 4

 (iv) −0.000 009 590 0

6 $\frac{22}{7}$, $\sqrt[3]{31}$, $154^{\frac{5}{22}}$, $43^{\frac{7}{23}}$

7 Error = −0.000 004 165, Relative error = −0.000 004 186

Exact value	Approximation	Error	Absolute error	Relative error	Absolute relative error	Percentage error
129.28	130	0.72	0.72	0.005 569 307	0.005 569 307	0.556 930 693
32.3	32	−0.3	0.3	−0.009 287 926	0.009 287 926	0.928 792 570
0.0078	0.008	0.0002	0.0002	0.025 641 026	0.025 641 026	2.564 102 564
0.0078	0.01	0.0022	0.0022	0.282 051 282	0.282 051 282	28.205 128 210
2 000 234	2 000 000	−234	234	−0.000 116 986	0.000 116 986	0.011 698 631

Exercise 1B (Page 13)

1 (i) 1.5 (to 1 d.p.)

 (ii) 3.9 (to 1 d.p.)

 (iii) 78.9000 (to 4 d.p.)

 (iv) 56.73 (to 2 d.p.)

2 (i) 100 (to 1 s.f.)

 (ii) 7860 (to 3 s.f.)

 (iii) 5000 (to 1 s.f.)

 (iv) 58 001 000 (to 5 s.f.)

3 (i) $3.05 \leqslant x < 3.15$

 (ii) 0.05

4 $32\,250 \leqslant x \leqslant 32\,349$ (given that x has to be an integer)

5 No, for example, x could equal 0.786 and so round to

 0.79 to 2 d.p.

6 23.95, the maximum possible absolute error is 0.04

7 (i) $56 \leqslant x \leqslant 64$

 (ii) $79.75 \leqslant x \leqslant 79.85$

 (iii) $0.9998 \leqslant x \leqslant 1$

8 (i) 1

 (ii) 0.125

9 (i) 0.02

 (ii) 0.1

10 Yes, the exact length of the course, x, satisfies $5 \leqslant x \leqslant 6\frac{1}{9}$.

11 (i) Relative error in $g = 10$ is $\frac{0.2}{9.8} = 0.0204$

 If $t = 4$, $h = 8g = 80$; error is 1.6

 Relative error is $\frac{1.6}{78.4} = 0.0204$

 (ii) h is calculated as $0.5 \times 9.8 \times 5^2 = 122.5$

 Range for h is 99.225

 $= 0.5 \times 9.8 \times 4.5^2 < h < 0.5 \times 9.8 \times 5.5^2 = 148.225$

 (iii) Maximum possible relative error $= \frac{122.5 - 99.225}{99.225}$

 $= 0.235.$

Exercise 1C (Page 17)

1 (i) $14.31 \leqslant x + y \leqslant 14.95$

 (ii) $5.81 \leqslant y - x \leqslant 6.45$

 (iii) $41.24 \leqslant xy \leqslant 47.025$

 (iv) $0.382\,775\,119 < \frac{x}{y} < 0.436\,469\,448$

 (Note that the lower bound has been rounded

 down and the upper bound rounded up to

 ensure that the given interval contains $\frac{x}{y}$.)

2 (i) $72\,385 \leqslant x + y \leqslant 72\,493$, $x + y$ is 72 000 (to 2 s.f.)

 (ii) $71\,706 \leqslant y - x \leqslant 71\,814$, $y - x$ is 72 000 (to 2 s.f.)

 (iii) $24\,136\,750 \leqslant xy \leqslant 24\,819\,256$,

 xy is 20 000 000 (to 1 s.f.)

 (iv) $0.004\,643\,16 \leqslant \frac{x}{y} \leqslant 0.047\,744\,63$,

 $\frac{x}{y}$ is 0.005 (to 1 s.f.)

3 (i) $0.3115 \leqslant x < 0.3125$, x is 0.312 (to 3 d.p.)

 (ii) $0.205 \leqslant y < 0.215$, y is 0.21 (to 2 d.p.)

 (iii) $0.5165 \leqslant x + y < 0.5275$, $x + y$ is 0.5 (to 1 d.p.)

 (iv) $0.0915 < x - y < 0.1075$, $x - y$ is 0.1 (to 1 d.p.)

 (v) $0.7215 \leqslant x + 2y < 0.7425$, $x + 2y$ is 0.7 (to 1 d.p.)

 (vi) $1.448\,837\,21 < \frac{x}{y} < 1.524\,390\,25$, $\frac{x}{y}$ is 1 (to 0 d.p.)

 (vii) $0.019\,891\,611 \leqslant x^2y < 0.020\,996\,094$,

 x^2y is 0.02 (to 2 d.p.)

4 (i) a is 1.2345 (to 4 d.p.) and b is 1.2346 (to 4 d.p.).

 (ii) $1.2346 - 1.2345 = 0.0001$

 The exact value of $b - a$ is 0.000 01.

 Percentage error = 900%

5 (i) $d = 49.96$, $a = 0.02$, $\beta = 49.98$

 Roots to 6 d.p. are 0.020 008 and 49.979 992

 Relative errors are -0.0004 and 0.000 000 16

 respectively.

 (ii) $\beta = 49.98$, $a = 0.020\,008$

 (iii) The second algorithm finds the larger root first,

 thus avoiding large relative errors. It then uses

 division rather than subtraction for the second

 root, preserving accuracy.

6 (i) Calculated value of $r = 1.168\,49$

 Interval for r is $1.138\,42 < r < 1.199\,44$

 (a) Maximum possible relative error

 $= \frac{1.168\,49 - 1.138\,42}{1.138\,42} = 0.026\,49$

 or $\frac{1.168\,49 - 1.199\,44}{1.199\,44} = -0.025\,73$

 So the maximum is 0.026 49.

 (b) r can be given to just 1 significant figure

 with certainty.

 (ii) Interval for r is $1.153\,35 < r < 1.183\,85$, so r is

 1.2 to 2 s.f.

(iii) Still some way short of 3 s.f. in part **(ii)** so try taking angles to be correct to the nearest 0.2°. The interval for r is $1.162\,40 < r < 1.174\,60$, which is still not accurate enough.

So try taking angles to be correct to the nearest 0.1°. Then the interval for r is $1.165\,44 < r < 1.171\,54$, which just gives 1.17 to 3 s.f.

x	$f(x)$	Change in x	Change in $f(x)$
6.1	−0.027 6167		
		−0.09	−0.000 857 043
6.01	−0.028 4737		
		−0.009	−0.000 087 912
6.001	−0.028 5616		
		−0.0009	−0.000 008 814
6.0001	−0.028 5704		

The function displays ill-conditioning near to $x = 1$ but not near to $x = 6$.

❓ (Page 21)

(i) If X is an overestimate then r_1 is positive; if Y is an underestimate then r_2 is negative. Therefore $r_1 - r_2$ will be a positive number larger than r_1 and $-r_2$. So the absolute relative error in $\dfrac{X}{Y}$ is greater than both the absolute relative error in X and the absolute relative error in Y.

(ii) This is the reverse of the situation in part **(i)**. This time r_1 is negative and r_2 is positive. Again, the absolute relative error in $\dfrac{X}{Y}$ is greater than both the absolute relative error in X and the absolute relative error in Y.

(iii) Now r_1 and r_2 are positive. The absolute relative error in $\dfrac{X}{Y}$ is less than the maximum of the absolute relative error in X and the absolute relative error in Y.

(iv) Both relative errors are negative. The absolute relative error in $\dfrac{X}{Y}$ is less than the maximum of the absolute relative error in X and the absolute relative error in Y.

❓ (Page 23)

x	$f(x)$	Change in x	Change in $f(x)$
1.1	−4.761 9048		
		−0.09	−44.989 339 02
1.01	−49.751 244		
		−0.009	−449.998 881 2
1.001	−499.750 12		
		−0.0009	−4499.999 888
1.0001	−4999.75		

❓ (Page 24)

From the graph you can see that around $x = 1$ and $x = -1$ small changes in x would result in large changes in $f(x)$.

Exercise 1D (Page 24)

1 **(i)** $r_1 = 0.002\,064\,447$

   (ii) $r_2 = -0.000\,375\,353$

   (iii) $0.001\,688\,319 \approx r_1 + r_2$

   (iv) $0.002\,440\,717 \approx r_1 - r_2$

   (v) $0.004\,133\,157 \approx 2r_1$

   (vi) $-0.001\,125\,637 \approx 3r_2$

   (vii) $0.002\,064\,447 = r_1$

   (viii) $0.000\,375\,494 \approx -r_2$

   (ix) $0.013\,023\,640 \approx 5r_1 - 7r_2$

   (x) $0.004\,510\,203 \approx 2r_1 - r_2$

2 Relative error in $T = 0.014\,492\,754$, error in $T^2 = 0.3475$

   relative error in $T^2 = 0.029\,195\,547$

   error in $\sqrt{T} = 0.013\,411\,131$,

   relative error in $\sqrt{T} = 0.007\,220\,31$

3 **(i)** Absolute error $= 0.000\,001\,338\,75$

   (ii) Absolute error $= 0.000\,000\,336\,29$

   The second student's approximation is better.

   (iii) The relative error in her approximation to $\tan 0.1$ is roughly the relative error in her approximation to $\sin 0.1$ minus the relative error in her approximation to $\cos 0.1$.

4 **(i)** $x = 0.36$ and $x = 0.81$

(ii) $x = 0.25$, absolute error $= 0.02667$,

relative error $= 0.053$

$x = 0.64$, absolute error $= 0.01333$,

relative error $= -0.017$

(iii) Relative error $= 0.00135$

(iv) $s = 1.01\sqrt{x}$, improved estimate $\approx 1.00005\sqrt{x}$

which has a relative error of 0.00005.

5 **(i)** $P_3 = 197.9949$ can be approximated by 198,

relative error $r_1 = 0.0000255$

$Q_3 = 280.0071$ can be approximated by 280,

relative error $r_2 = -0.0000255$

$\sqrt{2} = \dfrac{Q_3}{P_3} \approx \dfrac{140}{99}$, relative error $r_3 = -0.000051$,

$r_3 \approx r_2 - r_1$

(ii) For example, $P_4 = 1153.999$, $Q_4 = 1632.001$,

so $\sqrt{2} = \dfrac{Q_4}{P_4} \approx \dfrac{1632}{1154} = \dfrac{816}{577}$.

(iii) $(3 - 2\sqrt{2}) = 0.171573$, $(3 - 2\sqrt{2})^2 = 0.029437$,

$(3 - 2\sqrt{2})^3 = 0.005051$.

$(3 - 2\sqrt{2})^n$ tends to zero, so difference between

both P_n and Q_n and an integer gets small quickly.

Chapter 2

❓ (Page 29)

Simply substitute in the values.

❓ (Page 29)

For these values of x, $x^3 + 4$ and $4x^2 + x$ are the same

number, so these values are roots of the equation

$x^3 + 4 = 4x^2 + x$.

❓ (Page 30)

The graph of $y = x^3 - 4x^2 - x + 4$ crosses the x axis at

points with x co-ordinates that satisfy the equation

$x^3 - 4x^2 - x + 4 = 0$. As $x^3 - 4x^2 - x + 4 = 0$ is simply a

rearrangement of $x^3 + 4 = 4x^2 + x$ these will also be roots

of $x^3 + 4 = 4x^2 + x$.

❓ (Page 31)

Because the graph of most functions is an unbroken line.

Exercise 2A (Page 32)

1 $f(x) = x^3 - 3x + 1$,

$f(0.345) = 0.006064$, $f(0.355) = -0.02026$.

2 $f(x) = x^3 + x^2 + 5x + 2$,

$f(-0.45) = -0.13863$, $f(-0.35) = 0.329625$

3 $f(x) = x^3 - x^2 - 3x + 2$,

$f(0.615) = 0.009383$, $f(0.625) = -0.02148$

4 $f(x) = x^2 - 2$, $f(1.35) = -0.1775$, $f(1.45) = 0.1025$

5 $f(x) = \cos x - 2\sin x$,

$f(6.65) = 0.216187$, $f(6.75) = -0.00708$

6 0.7 (to 1 d.p.)

7 One possibility is $f(x) = (x - 2)(x - 3)$. For this

example there are two roots between $x = 1$ and $x = 4$.

Exercise 2B (Page 37)

1 1.3

2 0.7

3 $f(x) = x - \tan x$, $f(4) = 2.842179$, $f(4.5) = -0.13733$,

$f(4.25) = 2.2437$, $f(4.375) = 1.5244$,

$f(4.4375) = 0.8918$, $f(4.46875) = 0.4459$,

so the root is 4.5 to 1 d.p.

4 **(i)** $f(x) = x^3 + 0.5x^2 - 0.5x - 1.5$, $f(1) = -0.5$,

$f(1.2) = 0.348$, $f(1.1) = -0.114$,

$f(1.15) = 0.107125$, so the root is 1.1 to 1 d.p.

(ii) $f(x) = 1.5x \cos x - \sin x$, $f(1) = -0.03102$,

$f(0.8) = 0.11869$, $f(0.9) = 0.055847$,

$f(0.95) = 0.015483$, so the root is 1.0 to 1 d.p.

5 1.3

6 $f(h) = \cos\left((1 - h)\sqrt{2h - h^2} + \frac{1}{3}\right) + h - 1$,

$f(0.32) = -0.00654$, $f(0.33) = 0.004348$,

$f(0.325) = -0.00113$, $f(0.3275) = 0.001602$,

$f(0.32625) = 0.000234$, $f(0.325625) = -0.00045$,

so the root is 0.326 to 3 d.p.

7 **(i)** $f(x) = \dfrac{x(x^{10} - 1)}{x - 1} - 14$, $f(1.01) = -3.433165333$,

$f(1.09) = 2.560293392$, so the root is in the

interval $(1.01, 1.09)$.

(ii) $f(1.05) = -0.793\,212\,838$, $f(1.07) = 0.783\,599\,319$, $f(1.06) = -0.028\,357\,361$, so the root is in the interval $(1.06, 1.07)$. 1.065 is an approximation with maximum possible absolute error of 0.005.

8 (i) (a) $f(x) = x^3 + x - 1$, $f(0) = -1$, $f(1) = 1$ so the root is in the interval $(0, 1)$.

$f'(x) = 3x^2 + 1 > 0$, so there are no other roots.

(b) $f(0.5) = -0.375$, $f(0.75) = 0.171\,875$, $f(0.625) = -0.130\,867$ so the root is in the interval $(0.625, 0.75)$. The best estimate is the mid-point, 0.6875, with a maximum possible absolute error of 0.0625.

Four more steps.

(ii) (a) 0.005

(b) For example, $b = 1.234$, $B = 1.238$, second estimate $b = 1.498$, $B = 1.502$.

Activity 2.1 (Page 38)

The value displayed becomes closer and closer to 0.739\,085\,133.

See text that follows.

Activity 2.3 (Page 41)

The sequences are shown in the table.

r	(i)	(ii)	(iii)
0	1	1	1
1	0	1.8415	1.4207
2	-1.5708	0.4140	1.4059
3	–	1.6449	1.4108
4	–	0.9364	1.4092
5	–	1.8650	1.4098

The sequence shown in column **(iii)** appears to be converging to a value near to 1.410.
The sequence in column **(ii)** is oscillating and does not appear to be converging.

The sequence $x_{r+1} = \arcsin(x_r^2 - 1)$, $x_0 = 1$, the values of which are listed in column **(i)**, gives $x_2 = -1.5708$ and since $x_2^2 - 1 > 1$, the value of $\arcsin(x_2^2 - 1)$ is not defined.

Exercise 2C (Page 41)

1 (i) $5, -3.380\,52, -0.243\,575, -0.248\,51, -0.253\,75$; converges

(ii) $5, 2.449\,49, 1.857\,28, 1.690\,349, 1.640\,228$; converges

(iii) $5, 1.709\,976, 1.195\,813, 1.061\,421, 1.0200$; converges

(iv) $5, 1.570\,795, 0.319\,571, 0.063\,958, 0.012\,792$; converges

2 4.236\,07

3 (i) 0.453\,40

(ii) The sequence does not converge.

4 (i) 1.466

(ii) 0.618

(iii) Does not converge

(iv) Does not converge

Activity 2.4 (Page 43)

In both cases the sequences converges to 1.

See text that follows.

Activity 2.5 (Page 44)

The numbers get larger and larger.

See text that follows.

❷ (Page 45)

Rearrange and then factorise the quadratic to find its roots.
The sequence does not converge.

❷ (Page 48)

Consecutive iterations are on either side of the root, so they can be used to give interval estimates for the root.

Exercise 2D (Page 48)

1 $f(x) = 0.5\sin x - x + 3$, $f(0) = 3$, $f(2\pi) = -3.283\,185\,307$

The iterations are 2.5, 3.299 236 072, 2.921 504 358,

3.109 157 895, ... The root is 3.05 to 2 d.p.

2 **(i)** $x = 6 - \dfrac{5}{x}$ and $x = \dfrac{x^2 + 5}{6}$ can both be rearranged

to give $x^2 - 6x + 5 = 0$.

(ii) The two roots are 5 and 1.

(iii) (a) $f(x) = 6 - \dfrac{5}{x}$, $f'(x) = \dfrac{5}{x^2}$, $f'(5) = \frac{1}{5}$,

$f'(1) = 5$, so this formula will converge

to 5 but not to 1.

(b) $f(x) = \dfrac{x^2 + 5}{6}$, $f'(x) = \dfrac{x}{3}$, $f'(5) = \frac{5}{3}$,

$f'(1) = \frac{1}{3}$, so this formula will converge to 1

but not to 5.

(iv) (a) For example, if $x_0 = -3$ the iterations are

-3, 7.666 666 667, 5.347 826 087,

5.065 040 65, 5.012 841 091, 5.002 561 639.

(b) For example, if $x_0 = 0$ the iterations are

0.833 333 333, 0.949 074 074, 0.983 456 933,

0.994 531 257, 0.998 182 07, 0.999 394 574.

3 The equation is $x^2 - 3x + 2 = 0$, with roots 1 and 2.

(i) $f(x) = \dfrac{x^2 + 2}{3}$, $f'(x) = \dfrac{2x}{3}$, $f'(2) = \frac{4}{3}$, $f'(1) = \frac{2}{3}$, so

the sequence will converge to 1.

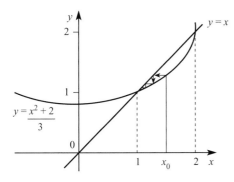

(ii) $f(x) = 3 - \dfrac{2}{x}$, $f'(x) = \dfrac{2}{x^2}$, $f'(2) = \frac{2}{4}$, $f'(1) = 2$ so

the sequence will converge to 2.

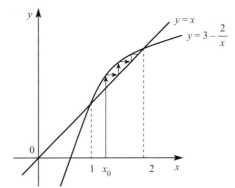

4 **(i)** The sequences obtained with the different

starting values are shown in the table.

x_0	x	x_2	x_3	x_4	x_5
1	2.000 000	2.125 000	2.229 213	2.319 484	2.399 619
4	4.015 625	4.031 068	4.046 335	4.061 429	4.076 356
5	5.008 000	5.015 962	5.023 886	5.031 772	5.039 621
10	10.001	10.002	10.003	10.004	10.005
20	20.000 13	20.000 25	20.000 37	20.000 50	20.000 62

(ii) $y = x$ is an asymptote to $y = x + \dfrac{1}{x^3}$.

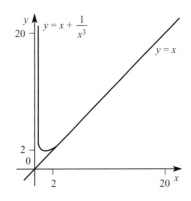

5 **(i)** With $f(x) = 100x - 101\cos x$, $f(0.7)$ is negative

and $f(0.8)$ is positive.

(ii) 0.743

❓ (Page 49)

The next iteration is where $y = 3x - 4.25$ crosses the x axis.

This is at $x = 1.416\,666\,667$.

The next value is 1.414 215 686.

? (Page 50)

The gradient of the tangent is found by evaluating the derivative at the x co-ordinate.

Activity 2.5 (Page 52)

1 The iterative formula is $x_{r+1} = x_r - \left(\dfrac{x_r^2 - 7}{2x_r}\right)$.

2 The sequence is 3, 2.666 666 667, 2.645 833 333,

2.645 751 312, 2.645 751 311, 2.645 751 311,

2.645 751 311.

$\sqrt{7}$ is 2.645 751 311 to 9 d.p.

3 The absolute errors in the first few terms are

0.354 248 689, 0.020 915 356, 8.202 23 × 10^{-5} and

1.335 96 × 10^{-9} respectively.

4 The convergence is very fast.

? (Page 53)

The first step uses the fact that dividing by a fraction is the same as multiplying by its reciprocal.

The second step puts the whole expression over a common denominator, $f(x_1) - f(x_0)$; so x_1 becomes

$\dfrac{x_1(f(x_1) - f(x_0))}{f(x_1) - f(x_0)}$.

The final step is to multiply out the numerator and cancel where appropriate.

Exercise 2E (Page 55)

1 $x_{r+1} = x_r - \left(\dfrac{x_r^4 - x_r^2 - 2}{4x_r^3 - 2x_r}\right)$. The iterations are 1.5,

1.422 619 048, 1.414 303 964, 1.414 213 573,

1.414 213 562. The root is 1.414 21 to 5 d.p.

2 (i) $x_{r+1} = x_r - \left(\dfrac{x_r^4 + x_r - 3}{4x_r^3 + 1}\right)$. The iterations are 1.5,

1.254 310 345, 1.172 277 657, 1.164 110 042,

1.164 035 147 and 1.164 035 14.

The root is 1.164 04 to 5 d.p.

(ii) $x_{r+1} = x_r - \left(\dfrac{x_r^4 - 2}{4x_r^3}\right)$. The iterations are 1.5,

1.273 148 148, 1.197 149 82, 1.189 285 812,

1.189 207 123 and 1.189 207 115.

The root is 1.189 21 to 5 d.p.

(iii) $x_{r+1} = x_r - \left(\dfrac{x_r^5 + x_r^4 + 3x_r - 2}{5x_r^4 + 4x_r^3 + 3}\right)$. The iterations are

1, 0.75, 0.621 806 854, 0.598 900 330,

0.598 366 517, 0.598 366 245 and 0.598 366 245.

The root is 0.598 37 to 5 d.p.

(iv) $x_{r+1} = x_r - \left(\dfrac{x_r + \sqrt{x_r} - 1}{1 + \dfrac{1}{2\sqrt{x_r}}}\right)$. The iterations are

1, 0.333 333 333, 0.381 197 846, 0.381 965 838,

0.381 966 011 and 0.381 966 011.

The root is 0.381 97 to 5 d.p.

3 $(x-1)^3(x-2) = 0$ rearranges to give

$x^4 - 5x^3 + 9x^2 - 7x + 2 = 0$.

$x_{r+1} = x_r - \left(\dfrac{x_r^4 - 5x_r^3 + 9x_r^2 - 7x_r + 2}{4x_r^3 - 15x_r^2 + 18x_r - 7}\right)$.

The iterations using the different starting values are shown in the table.

x_0	x_1	x_2	x_3	x_4	x_5
0.5	0.65	0.757 386 364	0.833 315 960	0.886 351 576	0.922 988 124
1.5	1.25	1.156 25	1.100 740 132	1.065 857 505	1.043 376 701
2.5	2.25	2.093 75	2.019 176 136	2.001 024 582	2.000 003 136

All converge to one of the two roots.

4 With the bisection method the iterations depend on the starting values chosen.

The iterative formula for the Newton–Raphson method is $f(x) = x^3 - 25$, $x_{r+1} = x_r - \left(\dfrac{x_r^3 - 25}{3x_r^2}\right)$.

The iterations with $x_0 = 4$ are 4, 3.1875,

2.945 197 36, 2.924 169 681, 2.924 017 746 and

2.924 017 738. The root is 2.924 018 to 6 d.p.

5 $x_{r+1} = x_r - \left(\dfrac{x_r^3 - 9x_r^2 + 6}{3x_r^2 - 18x_r}\right)$. The iterations are 0.8,

0.860 256 41, 0.858 466 313, 0.858 464 759,

0.858 464 759, 0.858 464 759 and 0.858 464 759.

The root is 0.858 464 8 to 7 d.p.

6 (i) (a) Diverges

(b) Converges, but slowly

(ii) $x_{r+1} = x_r - \left(\dfrac{x_r - 0.8(1 - x_r^3)}{1 + 2.4x_r^2}\right)$. The iterations are

0.6, 0.614 592, 0.614 43, 0.614 43, 0.614 43 and

0.614 43. The root is 0.614 33 to 5 s.f.

(iii) $f'(x) = -2.4x^2$, $f'(0.61443) = -0.90606$.

The negative sign indicates oscillation; a magnitude just less than 1 indicates slow convergence.

7 (i) $f(x) = x^4 + x - 3$

The iterations are 1.5, 1.3, 1.203914561, 1.169526676, 1.164272844, 1.164036588 and 1.164035141. The root is 1.16404 to 5 d.p.

(ii) $f(x) = x^4 - 2$

The iterations are 1.5, 1.3, 1.222398477, 1.193413415, 1.189378686, 1.189208023, 1.189207115 and 1.189207115.

The root is 1.18921 to 5 d.p.

(iii) $f(x) = \cos x - 0.6x$

The iterations are 1.1, 1, 0.959307991, 0.958260579, 0.9582519 and 0.958251898.

The root is 0.95825 to 5 d.p.

(iv) $f(x) = 2\cos x + 5x - 1$

The iterations are 0, −0.1, −0.196081634, −0.192543665, −0.192603634 and −0.192603672. The root is −0.19260 to 5 d.p.

8 $f(x) = \sin x - \cos 2x - 1$

The iterations are 0.5, 0.7, 0.896495094, 0.895931059, 0.895907477 and 0.895907481.

The root is 0.89591 to 5 d.p.

9 (i)

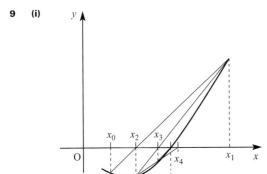

(ii) $f(x) = 3\sin x - x$, $f(2) = 0.72789228$, $f(3) = -2.576639976$, therefore the root is in the interval $(2, 3)$.

The iterations are 2, 3, 2.220270896, 2.268247329, 2.279114302, 2.278861621, 2.27886266, 2.27886266.
The root is 2.2789 to 4 d.p.

❓ (Page 58)

(i) Because it is a length and cannot be negative.

(ii) Similar triangles

(iii) First the denominators are cross multiplied. Then the brackets are multiplied out and the terms involving c are separated from those which do not involve c.

Then c is factorised from the terms it appears in and an expression for c is obtained by performing the appropriate division.

❓ (Page 60)

Becomes apparent from the graph; the chord used in the construction is always above the curve.

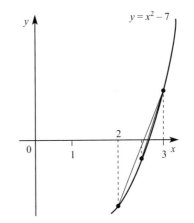

Activity 2.6 (Page 61)

1 The first eight iterations are 1.286978573, 1.377411095, 1.401486155, 1.407588997, 1.409116423, 1.409497482, 1.409592472 and 1.409616146.

The root is 1.4096 to 4 d.p. This can be confirmed by a sign-change check.

2 The absolute errors in the first eight iterations are

0.122 621 427, 0.032 188 905, 0.008 113 845,

0.002 011 003, 0.000 483 577, 0.000 102 518,

0.000 007 528 and 0.000 016 146.

Exercise 2F (Page 61)

1 (i)

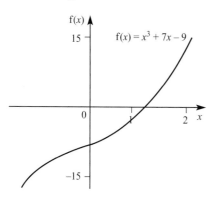

$f(x) = x^3 + 7x - 9$

From the graph there is a root in the interval

(1, 2). With starting values $a = 1$ and $b = 2$,

the approximations are 1.071 428 571,

1.090 324 884, 1.095 303 393, 1.096 613 46,

1.096 958 082, 1.097 048 73, 1.097 072 573 and

1.097 078 844.

The root is 1.097 to 3 d.p.

(ii)

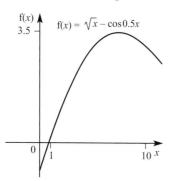

$f(x) = \sqrt{x} - \cos 0.5x$

From the graph there is a root in the interval

(0, 1). With starting values $a = 0$ and $b = 1$, the

approximations are 0.890 934 127,

0.855 447 139, 0.842 812 135, 0.838 174 263,

0.836 453 023, 0.835 811 625, 0.835 572 256,

0.835 482 873 and 0.835 449 489.

The root is 0.835 to 3 d.p.

(iii)

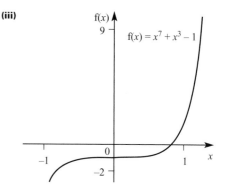

$f(x) = x^7 + x^3 - 1$

From the graph there is a root in the interval (0, 1).

With starting values $a = 0$ and $b = 1$, the

approximations are 0.5, 0.732 217 573,

0.820 831 263, 0.850 180 041, 0.859 248 911,

0.861 982 044 and 0.862 799 243.

The root is 0.9 to 1 d.p.

(iv)

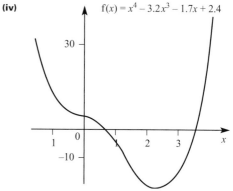

$f(x) = x^4 - 3.2x^3 - 1.7x + 2.4$

From the graph there is a root in the interval (0, 1).

With starting values $a = 0$ and $b = 1$, the

approximations are 0.615 384 615, 0.743 762 198,

0.763 475 647, 0.766 245 522, 0.766 629 353 and

0.766 629 353.

The root is 0.767 to 3 d.p.

2 (i) $f(x) = x^2 - 3x - 3$

From the graph there is a root in the

interval (−1, 0).

With starting values $a = -1$ and $b = 0$, the

approximations are −0.75, −0.789 473 684,

−0.791 208 791, −0.791 284 404 and

−0.791 287 697.

The root is −0.8 to 1 d.p. (this has an absolute

error less than 0.05).

(ii) $f(x) = x - \cos x$

From the graph there is a root in the interval $(0, 2)$.

With starting values $a = 0$ and $b = 2$,

the approximations are 0.585 454 928,

0.717 134 868, 0.736 255 683, 0.738 726 106 and

0.739 039 67.

The root is 0.7 to 1 d.p.

(iii) From the graph there is a root in the interval $(1, 2)$.

With starting values $a = 1$ and $b = 2$, the

approximations are 1.286 978 573, 1.377 411 095,

1.401 486 155, 1.407 588 997 and 1.409 116 423.

The root is 1.4 to 1 d.p.

3

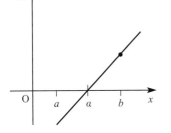

The first approximation is

$$\frac{a(mb + c) - b(ma + c)}{(mb + c) - (ma + c)} = \frac{c(a - b)}{m(b - a)}$$

$$= -\frac{c}{m}$$

The straight line joining $(a, f(a))$ to $(b, f(b))$ crosses

the x axis at the root, a.

Chapter 3

❓ (Page 65)

There are n strips of equal width spanning the distance

$b - a$.

Activity 3.1 (Page 67)

1   Estimate = 0.496

Exact value = 0.5

Error = –0.004

2   **(i)**   1.793

(ii)   1.799

Exercise 3A (Page 68)

1   **(i)**   0.507 531 26

(ii)   0.230 689 57

2   **(i)**   **(a)**   0.25, 0.3125, 0.3281

(b)   0.0312, 0.0389, 0.0408

(c)   2.7635, 2.4252, 2.3498

(ii)   Exact value $= \frac{1}{3}$

Errors are –0.083 333 333, –0.020 833 333 and

–0.005 208 333.

Each error is about a quarter of the previous one.

3 $n = 1$ and 2 only

$M_1 = 4.833 928$, $M_2 = 4.982 332$

❓ (Page 71)

Underestimating

Activity 3.2 (Page 72)

1   1.1

2   **(i)**   0.75

(ii)   0.819

(iii)   0.832

Exercise 3B (Page 73)

1   **(i)**   0.507 973 583

(ii)   0.221 545 548

2   **(i)**   **(a)**   0.5, 0.375, 0.3438

(b)   0.0619, 0.0465, 0.0427

(c)   1.4932, 2.1283, 2.2768

(ii)   Exact value $= \frac{1}{3}$

Errors are 0.166 666 667, 0.041 666 667 and

0.010 416 667.

Each error is about a quarter of the previous one.

3 $n = 1$, 2 and 4

$T_1 = 5.434 756$, $T_2 = 5.134 342$, $T_4 = 5.058 337$

4   0.361 56, 0.386 54, 0.392 51, 0.393 975

❓ (Page 74)

(i)   These are the definitions.

(ii)   Add the expressions for T_1 and M_1, divide by 2 and

then simplify.

(iii) One way to do this is to consider T_n and M_n as being a series of 'one strip' applications along the interval divided into n strips and use the result in **(ii)**.

❓ (Page 75)

You can see this if you imagine the line CD in figure 3.11(a) rotating about its mid-point until it is parallel and equal to the top of the trapezium.

❓ (Page 75)

Follows immediately. See also figure 3.11.

❓ (Page 76)

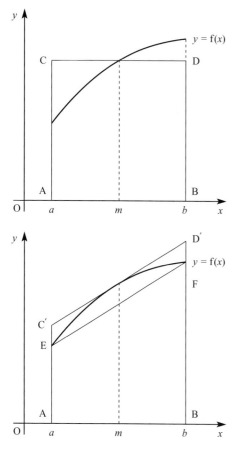

❓ (Page 78)

The average of M_n, M_n and T_n is $\dfrac{M_n + M_n + T_n}{3} = \dfrac{2M_n + T_n}{3}$.

Exercise 3C (Page 80)

1 $I = 1.11$ to 2 d.p.

2 $I = 1.1$ to 1 d.p.

3 2.936452, 2.936053, 2.936048

4 **(i)** 1

(ii) If f(0.3) becomes available then it is possible to calculate S_2 also.

5 Use $S_n = \dfrac{2M_n + T_n}{3}$ and $T_{2n} = \dfrac{T_n + M_n}{2}$

$\Rightarrow M_n = 2T_{2n} - T_n$.

6 **(i)** **(a)** $T_1 = 47.668$

(b) $M_1 = 44.092$

(c) $S_1 = 45.284$

(ii) $S_2 = 45.279$, $S_4 = 45.278$

7 **(i) and (ii)**

$T_1 = 3.236068$	$S_1 = 2.964307$
$M_1 = 2.828427$	
$T_2 = 3.032248$	$S_2 = 2.957956$
$M_2 = 2.920810$	
$T_4 = 2.976529$	$S_4 = 2.957883$
$M_4 = 2.948561$	

(iii) **(a)** 2.96 looks justified, to 2 d.p.

(b) Error in T_1 is 0.28, error in M_1 is –0.13, error in T_2 is 0.07, error in M_2 is –0.04, error in T_4 is 0.02, error in M_4 is –0.01

Chapter 4

❓ (Page 84)

Use two points to find the gradient and another point to find the y intercept.

❓ (Page 86)

It would need more rows and columns.

❓ (Page 88)

The $(n + 1)$th differences are the differences between the nth differences!

Exercise 4A (Page 89)

1

x_i	f_i	Δf_i	$\Delta^2 f_i$	$\Delta^3 f_i$	$\Delta^4 f_i$
3	21				
		−10			
5	11		13		
		3		−22	
7	14		−9		39
		−6		17	
9	8		8		
		2			
11	10				

2

x_i	f_i	Δf_i	$\Delta^2 f_i$	$\Delta^3 f_i$	$\Delta^4 f_i$
−3	0				
		4			
0	4		3		
		7		0	
3	11		3		0
		10		0	
6	21		3		
		13			
9	34				

3 (i) −0.25, 0, 0.25, 0.5, 0.75, 1.0, 1.25, 1.5

 (ii) 1.0, 1.1, 1.2, 1.3, 1.4, 1.5, 1.6, 1.7, 1.8, 1.9, 2.0

 (iii) 0, 0.01, 0.02, 0.03, 0.04, 0.05, 0.06, 0.07, 0.08, 0.09, 0.1

 (iv) 1.0, 1.125, 1.25, 1.375, 1.5, 1.625, 1.75, 1.875, 2.0

 (v) −2, −1, 0, 1, 2

4

x_i	f_i	Δf_i	$\Delta^2 f_i$	$\Delta^3 f_i$	$\Delta^4 f_i$	$\Delta^5 f_i$
0	0					
		−0.112				
0.2	−0.112		−0.192			
		−0.304		0.048		
0.4	−0.416		−0.144		0	
		−0.448		0.048		0
0.6	−0.864		−0.096		0	
		−0.544		0.048		
0.8	−1.408		−0.048			
		−0.592				
1	−2					

5 **(i)**

x_i	f_i	Δf_i	$\Delta^2 f_i$	$\Delta^3 f_i$	$\Delta^4 f_i$	$\Delta^5 f_i$
0	0					
		0.0001				
0.1	0.0001		0.0014			
		0.0015		0.0036		
0.2	0.0016		0.0050		0.0024	
		0.0065		0.0060		0
0.3	0.0081		0.0110		0.0024	
		0.0175		0.0084		
0.4	0.0256		0.0194			
		0.0369				
0.5	0.0625					

(ii)

x_i	f_i	Δf_i	$\Delta^2 f_i$	$\Delta^3 f_i$	$\Delta^4 f_i$	$\Delta^5 f_i$
0.0	0.000					
		0.000				
0.1	0.000		0.002			
		0.002		0.002		
0.2	0.002		0.004		0.006	
		0.006		0.008		−0.007
0.3	0.008		0.012		−0.001	
		0.018		0.007		
0.4	0.026		0.019			
		0.037				
0.5	0.063					

The fourth differences column is no longer constant so the Newton interpolating polynomial of degree 4 does not look like a good fit, even though the data is from a polynomial of degree 4.

6

x_i	f_i	Δf_i	$\Delta^2 f_i$	$\Delta^3 f_i$	$\Delta^4 f_i$	$\Delta^5 f_i$
0.0	0.000					
		0.199				
0.2	0.199		−0.009			
		0.190		−0.005		
0.4	0.389		−0.014		−0.005	
		0.176		−0.010		0.011
0.6	0.565		−0.024		0.006	
		0.152		−0.004		
0.8	0.717		−0.028			
		0.124				
1	0.841					

The maximum error in the f_i column is 0.0005, in the first difference column 0.001, in the second difference column 0.002, in the third difference column 0.004, in the fourth difference column 0.008 and in the fifth difference column 0.0016.

7 **(i)** $\Delta^2 f_0 = \Delta f_1 - \Delta f_0$

$\quad\quad = (f_2 - f_1) - (f_1 - f_0)$

$\quad\quad = f_2 - 2f_1 + f_0$

(ii) $\Delta^3 f_0 = \Delta^2 f_1 - \Delta^2 f_0$

$\quad\quad = (f_3 - 2f_2 + f_1) - (f_2 - 2f_1 + f_0)$

$\quad\quad = f_3 - 3f_2 + 3f_1 - f_0$

❓ (Page 91)

Two points for a straight line, three for a quadratic, four for a cubic. A polynomial of degree $n-1$ or less.

❓ (Page 92)

All the terms after the cubic term are zero since $(x_3 - x_3)$ appears in the numerator. The result follows using $(x_3 - x_2) = h$, $(x_3 - x_1) = 2h$, $(x_3 - x_0) = 3h$ and relationships such as $f_3 = f_2 + \Delta f_2$, $\Delta f_2 = \Delta f_1 + \Delta^2 f_1$.

❓ (Page 94)

Because the highest power of x is 1.

$$f(a) = \frac{A(a-b)}{a-b} + \frac{B(a-a)}{b-a} = A \qquad f(b) = \frac{A(b-b)}{a-b} + \frac{B(b-a)}{b-a} = B$$

❓ (Page 94)

Because the highest power of x is 2.

$$f(a) = \frac{A(a-b)(a-c)}{(a-b)(a-c)} + \frac{B(a-c)(a-a)}{(b-c)(b-a)} + \frac{C(a-a)(a-b)}{(c-a)(c-b)} = A$$

$$f(b) = \frac{A(b-b)(b-c)}{(a-b)(a-c)} + \frac{B(b-c)(b-a)}{(b-c)(b-a)} + \frac{C(b-a)(b-b)}{(c-a)(c-b)} = B$$

$$f(c) = \frac{A(c-b)(c-c)}{(a-b)(a-c)} + \frac{B(c-c)(c-a)}{(b-c)(b-a)} + \frac{C(c-a)(c-b)}{(c-a)(c-b)} = C$$

❓ (Page 94)

$$f(x) = \frac{A(x-b)(x-c)(x-d)}{(a-b)(a-c)(a-d)} + \frac{B(x-c)(x-d)(x-a)}{(b-c)(b-d)(b-a)} + \frac{C(x-d)(x-a)(x-b)}{(c-d)(c-a)(c-b)} + \frac{D(x-a)(x-b)(x-c)}{(d-a)(d-b)(d-c)}$$

Exercise 4B (Page 94)

1 (i)

x_i	f_i	Δf_i	$\Delta^2 f_i$	$\Delta^3 f_i$	$\Delta^4 f_i$	$\Delta^5 f_i$	$\Delta^6 f_i$
1.20	29						
		−23					
1.25	6		17				
		−6		−11			
1.30	0		6		5		
		0		−6		0	
1.35	0		0		5		0
		0		−1		0	
1.40	0		−1		5		
		−1		4			
1.45	−1		3				
		2					
1.50	1						

(ii) A polynomial of degree 4 is required for an exact fit.

2 $f(x) = 3x + 1$

3 $f(x) = x^2 + x + 1$

4   (i) $f(x) = 12 - \dfrac{67x}{6} + \dfrac{7x^2}{2} - \dfrac{x^3}{3}$

   (ii) $f(4.1) \approx 2.078$

5   (i)   degree 3   (ii) $f(3.2) \approx 29.368$

6   0.186

7   (i) $f(x) = 2x + 2$ (ii) $f(x) = -x^2 + 3x + 1$

   (iii) $f(x) = x^3 + x^2 + x + 1$

8   (i)

x_i	f_i	Δf_i	$\Delta^2 f_i$	$\Delta^3 f_i$
0	−3			
		15		
1	12		−8	
		7		6
2	19		−2	
		5		6
3	24		4	
		9		
4	33			

   (ii) $f(x) = x^3 - 7x^2 + 21x - 3$

   (iii) $f(0.145) = -0.099\,13$, $f(0.155) = 0.090\,549$

   (iv) $70\frac{2}{3}$

Exercise 4C (Page 100)

1   (i) $5x^2 - 32x + 59$

   (ii) $\dfrac{19x^3}{6} - \dfrac{47x^2}{2} + \dfrac{302x}{6} - 17$

   (iii) $3 + 10x - 2x^2$

2   (i)   7   (ii)   17.5

   (iii)   0   (iv)   14

   (v)   14   (vi)   14.625

   The last three answers are similar because

   approximations close to the point of interest are used.

3   (i)

x_i	f_i	Δf_i	$\Delta^2 f_i$	$\Delta^3 f_i$
0	1.5557			
		−0.4915		
1	1.0642		0.4427	
		−0.0488		−0.1039
2	1.0154		0.3388	
		0.29		
3	1.3054			

The second differences are substantially different.

   (ii) $f(x) = 1.5557 - 0.7475x + 0.2733x^2 - 0.0173x^3$

   $f(1.5) = 0.9910$, $f'(1.5) = -0.044\,38$

   (iii)   The interpolating cubic is clearly not exactly
   right; it could, however, be a good approximation.
   More data is needed to be sure.

4   (i)

x_i	f_i	Δf_i	$\Delta^2 f_i$	$\Delta^3 f_i$	$\Delta^4 f_i$	$\Delta^5 f_i$
0	0.2					
		1.6				
1	1.8		2.7			
		4.3		1.1		
2	6.1		3.8		0.1	
		8.1		1.2		−0.1
3	14.2		5.0		0.0	
		13.1		1.2		
4	27.3		6.2			
		19.3				
5	46.6					

The third differences are nearly constant so a
cubic is a good approximation.

   (ii)   73.3; this is extrapolation. The data is being
   used to predict the value of the function
   outside the given values so it is less reliable.

   (iii)   The cubic approximation gives $f(2.5) \approx 9.606\,25$.
   This is an interpolation, the data is being used to
   predict the value of the function between two
   given values. It is more reliable.

5   (i)   linear 3.266, quadratic 3.2452, cubic 3.252\,56,
   quartic 3.249\,392

   $f(0.8) = 3.25$ to 2 d.p. seems reasonable

   (ii)   The maximum possible error in each value of f
   is 0.05, this means that the first differences have
   a maximum possible absolute error of 0.1 and
   the second differences 0.2. This suggests that it
   is probably not reasonable to assume that the
   estimate of $f(0.8)$ is correct to 2 decimal places.

Chapter 5

❓ (Page 104)

The gradient of the chord gets closer to the gradient of the tangent as h decreases.

❓ (Page 104)

Because h is added to x, so $x + h$ is forward of x.

❓ (Page 107)

Because it uses function values on *both* sides of x.

One possible example of a graph of a function for which the forward difference approximation is better than the central difference approximation is shown below. The gradient of BC is clearly closer to $f'(x)$ than the gradient of AC.

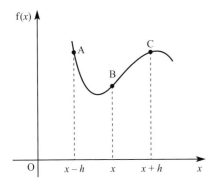

Exercise 5A (Page 110)

1 The forward difference approximations to $f'(1)$ are 7.4416, 6.1051 and 5.525 631 25. The exact value is 5, so the errors are 2.4416, 1.1051 and 0.525 631 25, which seem to be roughly halving.

The central difference approximations to $f'(1)$ are 5.4016, 5.1001 and 5.025 006 25. The exact value is 5, so the errors are 0.4016, 0.1001 and 0.025 006 25, which seem to be roughly quartering.

The forward difference approximations to $f'(1.5)$ are 33.0241, 28.9201, 27.057 193 75. The exact value is 25.3125, so the errors are 7.7116, 3.6076 and 1.744 693 75, which seem to be roughly halving.

The central difference approximations to $f'(1.5)$ are 26.2141, 25.5376 and 25.368 756 25. The exact value is 25.3125, so the errors are 0.9016, 0.2251, 0.056 256 25, which seem to be roughly quartering.

2 The forward difference approximations to $f'(0)$ are −0.099 667 111, −0.019 997 333 and −0.003 999 979.

The central difference approximations to $f'(0)$ are 0, 0 and 0. This is because $\cos x = \cos(-x)$.

The forward difference approximations to $f'(1.5)$ are −0.997 908 48, −0.998 643 565 and −0.997 767 294.

The central difference approximations to $f'(1.5)$ are −0.990 858 307, −0.997 229 009 and −0.997 484 347.

3 $f(1.55) = 48.078 482 48$, $f(1.56) = 92.620 496 32$.

Change in x is about 0.6%, change in $f(x)$ is about 93%. This is due to the steep gradient of $f(x) = \tan x$ around $x = \dfrac{\pi}{2}$.

4 (i) $f(0.001) = 0.993 116 05$, $f(0.000 01) = 0.999 884 88$, $f(0.000 000 1) = 0.999 998 39$, $f(0.000 000 001) = 0.999 999 98$.

(ii) Estimates are −6.883 951 579, −11.512 262 75, −16.118 082 66 and −20.723 265 66 suggesting that the function has a vertical ('infinite negative') gradient at $x = 0$.

(iii) With such a calculator the estimates obtained would have been −6.88, −12, 0 and 0 which may have given the impression of a sequence tending to zero. It may have lead to an incorrect belief that $f'(0) = 0$.

When making h smaller and smaller in this kind of calculation even more accurate calculators and computers will eventually give misleading results. It just happens earlier for less accurate ones.

5 (i) Both the forward and central difference approximations to $f'(0.5)$ are −0.4.

(ii) The forward difference approximation to $f'(0.25)$ is −0.4; the central difference approximation is 0.

The forward difference approximation to $f'(0.75)$ is 0.4; the central difference approximation is 0.

The forward difference approximation to $f''(1.5)$ is 1.6, the central difference approximation is 0.

(iii) There is not much agreement between the two approximations.

Chapter 6

❓ (Page 114)

Because the absolute error must be decreasing for the sequence to converge.

❓ (Page 114)

No

❓ (Page 114)

$$\frac{\text{absolute error in } x_1}{(\text{absolute error in } x_0)^3} \approx k, \frac{\text{absolute error in } x_2}{(\text{absolute error in } x_1)^3} \approx k,$$

$$\frac{\text{absolute error in } x_3}{(\text{absolute error in } x_2)^3} \approx k, \dots$$

❓ (Page 115)

The ratios are both 0.1.

Activity 6.1 (Page 117)

1   You can see from the diagram that

$$\frac{x_2 - x_1}{x_1 - x_0} = \frac{-(k\varepsilon - k^2\varepsilon)}{-(\varepsilon - k\varepsilon)} = \frac{k\varepsilon(1 - k)}{\varepsilon(1 - k)} = k.$$

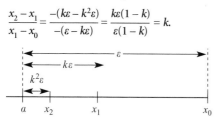

2   You can see from the diagram that

$$\frac{x_2 - x_1}{x_1 - x_0} = -\frac{k^2\varepsilon + k\varepsilon}{\varepsilon + k\varepsilon} = -\frac{k\varepsilon(1 + k)}{\varepsilon(1 + k)} = -k.$$

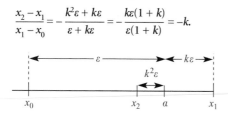

❓ (Page 120)

Sometimes the absolute error is so small that ordinary computing devices such as computers and calculators cannot distinguish it from zero. Therefore, such numbers cannot be used as the denominators in fractions.

Exercise 6A (page 121)

1   (i)   The ratios of differences are all 0.1.

(ii)   The ratios of differences are all 0.5.

(iii)   The ratios of differences are all –0.5.

(iv)   The ratios of differences are all 0.3, to 1 d.p.

(v)   The ratios of differences are all 0.1, to 1 d.p.

2   The ratios of differences are all 0.31, to 2 d.p.

3   The ratios of differences are all –0.172 to 3 d.p.

$f'(x) = -\dfrac{1}{x^2}$, $f'(2.41) = -0.172$ to 3 d.p.

4   In each case $\dfrac{\text{Absolute error in } x_1}{(\text{Absolute error in } x_0)^2}$,

$\dfrac{\text{Absolute error in } x_2}{(\text{Absolute error in } x_1)^2}, \dfrac{\text{Absolute error in } x_3}{(\text{Absolute error in } x_2)^2}, \dots$

are given below, calculated using the last term in the sequence as the limit. The fact that these numbers are roughly the same in each case is evidence of second-order convergence.

(i)   1.142 156 348, 1.279 535 62, 1.345 973 808

(ii)   0.799 798 817, 1.011 399 148, 1.102 386 433

(iii)   0.191 448 293, 0.206 575 064.

It is not possible to give the next value due to reaching the limits of accuracy of calculating devices: the absolute error in x_3 is extremely close to zero.

(iv)   –0.199 382 5, –0.181 681 357.

It is not possible to give the next value due to reaching the limits of accuracy of calculating devices: the absolute error in x_3 is extremely close to zero.

? (Page 124)

Simpson's rule is a fourth-order method so, when n is doubled, the subsequent error gets 16 times smaller. Therefore, the sequence of approximations obtained by repeatedly doubling n has first-order convergence with $k = \frac{1}{16}$. The subsequent ratios of differences will be close to $\frac{1}{16}$, as described earlier in the chapter.

? (Page 126)

1 $S_{64} \approx S_{32} + \frac{1}{16}(S_{32} - S_{16})$

2 $S_{128} \approx S_{32} + \frac{1}{16}(S_{32} - S_{16}) + \frac{1}{16^2}(S_{32} - S_{16})$

3 $S_{32} + \frac{1}{16}(S_{32} - S_{16}) + \frac{1}{16^2}(S_{32} - S_{16}) + \frac{1}{16^3}(S_{32} - S_{16}) + \dots$

$= S_{32} + (S_{32} - S_{16})\left(\frac{1}{16} + \frac{1}{16^2} + \frac{1}{16^3} + \dots\right)$

$= S_{32} + \dfrac{S_{32} - S_{16}}{15}$

Exercise 6B (Page 128)

1 (i) 0.248 954 392   (ii) 0.243 247 306

   (iii) 0.062 587 483

2 (i) 4.11 to 2 d.p.   (ii) 10.5 to 1 d.p.

   (iii) 5.02 to 2 d.p.

3 (i) $I = \dfrac{a^3}{3}$

   (a) $T_1 = \dfrac{a^3}{2}$, error $= \dfrac{a^3}{6}$

   (b) $M_1 = \dfrac{a^3}{4}$, error $= -\dfrac{a^3}{12}$

   $S_1 = \dfrac{a^3}{3}$, error $= 0$ so the value of S_1 is exact

   (ii) $T_1 = 0.681\,25$, $M_1 = 0.725\,48$

   $S_1 = 0.710\,73$

   $T_2 = 0.703\,36$, $M_2 = 0.713\,08$, $S_2 = 0.709\,84$

   Extrapolating shows that 0.710 to 3 d.p. is reasonable.

Exercise 6C (Page 131)

1 5.0 to 1 d.p.

2 1.17 to 2 d.p.

3 (i) f$'$(2) estimates: 0.119, 0.1212, 0.1223

   Differences: 0.0022 and 0.0011 so differences are halving

   Best estimate $= 0.1223 + 0.0011(0.5 + 0.5^2 + \dots)$

   $= 0.1234$

(ii) f$'$(2) estimates: 0.123 275, 0.123 375, 0.1234

Differences: 0.0001 and 0.000 025 so differences are reducing by a factor of 0.25

Best estimate

$= 0.1234 + 0.000\,025(0.25 + 0.25^2 + \dots)$

$= 0.123\,408$

6 decimal places are not justified as f(x) is only given to 5 decimal places. Can justify 0.1234 or (just) 0.123 41.

(iii) Central difference estimates are generally more accurate but central difference method cannot be used at the end of an interval. So use central difference at 1.8 and forward difference at 1.6.

4 (i) The ratios of differences are approximately 0.5.

   Best estimate

   $= 5.5693 + (-0.0242)(0.5 + 0.5^2 + \dots)$

   $= 5.5451$

   6 to 1 s.f. Cannot give 2 significant figures, could be 5.5 or 5.6.

(ii) The ratios of differences are approximately 0.25.

   Best estimate

   $= 11.090\,910 + (-0.001\,665)(0.25 + 0.25^2 + \dots)$

   $= 11.090\,355$

   11.09 to 4 s.f.

(iii) The forward difference method is a first-order method; the central difference method is a second-order method.

5 (i) $S_1 = 0.443\,893\,333$, $S_2 = 0.456\,093\,333$

   Best estimate $= 0.456\,093\,333 + (0.456\,093\,333 - 0.443\,893\,333)(0.0625 + 0.0625^2 + \dots)$

   $= 0.456\,906\,667$

   0.46 to 2 d.p. looks reliable

(ii) With $h = 0.4$ the estimate is 1.145; with $h = 0.2$ the estimate is 0.849 75.

   Best estimate

   $= 0.849\,75 + (0.849\,75 - 1.145)(0.25 + 0.25^2 + \dots)$

   $= 0.751\,333\,333$.

   0.8 to 1 d.p. should be reliable but only just

? (Page 124)

Simpson's rule is a fourth-order method so, when n is doubled, the subsequent error gets 16 times smaller. Therefore, the sequence of approximations obtained by repeatedly doubling n has first-order convergence with $k = \frac{1}{16}$. The subsequent ratios of differences will be close to $\frac{1}{16}$, as described earlier in the chapter.

? (Page 126)

1   $S_{64} \approx S_{32} + \frac{1}{16}(S_{32} - S_{16})$

2   $S_{128} \approx S_{32} + \frac{1}{16}(S_{32} - S_{16}) + \frac{1}{16^2}(S_{32} - S_{16})$

3   $S_{32} + \frac{1}{16}(S_{32} - S_{16}) + \frac{1}{16^2}(S_{32} - S_{16}) + \frac{1}{16^3}(S_{32} - S_{16}) + \dots$

$= S_{32} + (S_{32} - S_{16})\left(\frac{1}{16} + \frac{1}{16^2} + \frac{1}{16^3} + \dots\right)$

$= S_{32} + \frac{S_{32} - S_{16}}{15}$

Exercise 6B (Page 128)

1   (i)   0.248 954 392   (ii)   0.243 247 306

    (iii) 0.062 587 483

2   (i)   4.11 to 2 d.p.   (ii)   10.5 to 1 d.p.

    (iii) 5.02 to 2 d.p.

3   (i) $I = \dfrac{a^3}{3}$

       (a) $T_1 = \dfrac{a^3}{2}$, error $= \dfrac{a^3}{6}$

       (b) $M_1 = \dfrac{a^3}{4}$, error $= -\dfrac{a^3}{12}$

       $S_1 = \dfrac{a^3}{3}$, error $= 0$ so the value of S_1 is exact

    (ii) $T_1 = 0.681\,25$, $M_1 = 0.725\,48$

       $S_1 = 0.710\,73$

       $T_2 = 0.703\,36$, $M_2 = 0.713\,08$, $S_2 = 0.709\,84$

       Extrapolating shows that 0.710 to 3 d.p. is reasonable.

Exercise 6C (Page 131)

1   5.0 to 1 d.p.

2   1.17 to 2 d.p.

3   (i)   f′(2) estimates: 0.119, 0.1212, 0.1223

       Differences: 0.0022 and 0.0011 so differences are halving

       Best estimate $= 0.1223 + 0.0011(0.5 + 0.5^2 + \dots)$

       $= 0.1234$

(ii)   f′(2) estimates: 0.123 275, 0.123 375, 0.1234

    Differences: 0.0001 and 0.000 025 so differences are reducing by a factor of 0.25

    Best estimate

    $= 0.1234 + 0.000\,025(0.25 + 0.25^2 + \dots)$

    $= 0.123\,408$

    6 decimal places are not justified as f(x) is only given to 5 decimal places. Can justify 0.1234 or (just) 0.123 41.

(iii) Central difference estimates are generally more accurate but central difference method cannot be used at the end of an interval. So use central difference at 1.8 and forward difference at 1.6.

4   (i)   The ratios of differences are approximately 0.5.

       Best estimate

       $= 5.5693 + (-0.0242)(0.5 + 0.5^2 + \dots)$

       $= 5.5451$

       6 to 1 s.f. Cannot give 2 significant figures, could be 5.5 or 5.6.

    (ii) The ratios of differences are approximately 0.25.

       Best estimate

       $= 11.090\,910 + (-0.001\,665)(0.25 + 0.25^2 + \dots)$

       $= 11.090\,355$

       11.09 to 4 s.f.

    (iii) The forward difference method is a first-order method; the central difference method is a second-order method.

5   (i) $S_1 = 0.443\,893\,333$, $S_2 = 0.456\,093\,333$

       Best estimate $= 0.456\,093\,333 + (0.456\,093\,333 - 0.443\,893\,333)(0.0625 + 0.0625^2 + \dots)$

       $= 0.456\,906\,667$

       0.46 to 2 d.p. looks reliable

    (ii) With $h = 0.4$ the estimate is 1.145; with $h = 0.2$ the estimate is 0.849 75.

       Best estimate

       $= 0.849\,75 + (0.849\,75 - 1.145)(0.25 + 0.25^2$

       $= 0.751\,333\,333$.

       0.8 to 1 d.p. should be reliable but only j^r

Index